SCHOLASTIC

100 SCIENCE LESSONS

Terms and conditions

IMPORTANT – PERMITTED USE AND WARNINGS – READ CAREFULLY BEFORE USING

IF YOU ACCEPT THE ABOVE CONDITIONS YOU MAY PROCEED TO USE THE CD-ROM.

Recommended system requirements:

- Windows: XP (Service Pack 3), Vista (Service Pack 2), Windows 7 or Windows 8 with 2.33GHz processor
- Mac: OS 10.6 to 10.8 with Intel Core™ Duo processor
- 1GB RAM (recommended)
- 1024 x 768 Screen resolution
- CD-ROM drive (24x speed recommended)
- 16-bit sound card
- Adobe Reader (version 9 recommended for Mac users)
- Broadband internet connections (for installation and updates)

For all technical support queries, please phone Scholastic Customer Services on 0845 6039091.

Book End, Range Road, Witney, Oxfordshire, OX29 0YD
www.scholastic.co.uk

© 2014, Scholastic Ltd

23456789 4567890123

British Library Cataloguing-in-Publication Data
A catalogue record for this book is available from the
British Library.

ISBN 978-1407-12766-8
Printed by Bell & Bain Ltd, Glasgow

Due to the nature of the web we cannot guarantee
the content or links of any site mentioned. We strongly
recommend that teachers check websites before using
them in the classroom.

Extracts from *The National Curriculum in England, Science
Programme of Study* © Crown Copyright. Reproduced
under the terms of the Open Government Licence
(OGL). http://www.nationalarchives.gov.uk/doc/open-
government-licence/open-government-licence.htm

Author
Roger Smith

Consultant
Juliet Gladston

Series Editor
Peter Riley

Editorial team
Rachel Morgan, Pollyanna Poulter, Melissa Somers,
Kate Soar and Margaret Eaton

Cover Design
Andrea Lewis

Design Team
Sarah Garbett, Shelley Best and Andrea Lewis

CD-ROM development
Hannah Barnett, Phil Crothers, MWA Technologies
Private Ltd

Typesetting
Tracey Camden

Illustrations
Jim Peacock

Contents

Introduction

About the series

The *100 Science Lessons* series is designed to meet the requirements of the 2014 Curriculum, Science Programmes of Study. There are six books in the series, Years 1–6, and each book contains lesson plans, resources and ideas matched to the new curriculum. It can be a complex task to ensure that a progressive and appropriate curriculum is followed in all year groups; this series has been carefully structured to ensure that a progressive and appropriate curriculum is followed throughout.

About the new curriculum

The curriculum documentation for Science provides a single-year programme of study for each year in Key Stage 1 and 2. However schools are only required to teach the relevant programmes of study by the end of the key stage and can approach their curriculum planning with greater flexibility than ever before in the following ways. Within each key stage they can introduce content earlier or later than set out in the programme of study and they can introduce key stage content during an earlier key stage if appropriate. Whatever plan is used the school curriculum for science must be set out on a year-by-year basis and made available online.

Knowledge and conceptual understanding

The national curriculum for science aims to ensure that all children develop scientific knowledge and conceptual understanding through the specific disciplines of Biology (Plants, Animals including humans, Seasonal changes, Living things and their habitats, Evolution and inheritance), Chemistry (Everyday materials, Uses of everyday materials, Rocks, States of matter, Properties and changes of materials) and Physics (Seasonal changes, Light, Forces and magnets, Sound, Electricity, Earth and space). It is vitally important that the children develop a secure understanding of each key block of knowledge and its concepts in order to progress to the next stage. As they do so they should also be familiar with and use technical terminology accurately and precisely and build up an extended specialist vocabulary. Equally they should also apply their mathematical knowledge to their understanding of science including collecting, presenting and analysing data.

The nature, processes and methods of science

The requirements needed for the understanding of the nature, processes and methods of science are set out at the beginning of Key Stage 1, Lower Key Stage 2 and Upper Key Stage 2 in a section called Working scientifically. This section of the curriculum replaces the Science enquiry section of the previous science curriculum. It is important that Working scientifically is not taught as a separate strand and guidance is given in the non-statutory notes to help embed it in the scientific content of each area of the programme of study. In the working scientifically section the children are introduced to a range of types of scientific enquiry. These include observing over time, classifying and grouping, identifying, comparative and fair testing (making controlled investigations), pattern seeking and researching using secondary sources. The questions used to stimulate the enquiry should be answered by the children through collecting, presenting and analysing data and drawing conclusions from their findings.

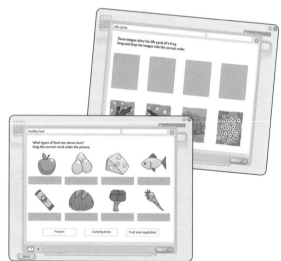

■ SCHOLASTIC

About the book

This book is divided into six chapters; each chapter contains a half-term's work and is based around one of the content areas in the programme of study. Each chapter follows the same structure:

Chapter introduction

At the start of each chapter there is an introduction with the following features. This includes:

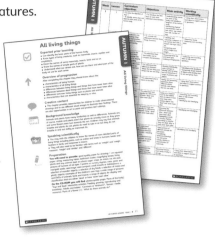

- **Expected prior learning:** What the children are expected to know before starting the work in the chapter.
- **Overview of progression:** A brief explanation of how the children progress through the chapter.
- **Creative context:** How the chapter could link to other curriculum areas.
- **Background knowledge:** A section explaining scientific terms and suchlike to enhance your subject knowledge, where required.
- **Speaking scientifically:** A section highlighting some of the key words featured in the chapter for building up the children's scientific vocabulary. This is also a feature of every lesson (see below).
- **Preparation:** Any resources required for the teaching of the chapter, including things that need to be sourced or prepared and the content that can be located on the CD-ROM. As part of the preparation of all practical work you should consult your school's policies on practical work and select activities for which you are confident to take responsibility. The ASE *Be Safe Forth Edition* gives very useful guidance on health and safety issues in primary science.
- **Chapter at a glance:** This is a table that summarises the content of each lesson, including: the curriculum objectives, lesson objectives, the main activity or activities and the working scientifically statutory requirements that are featured in each lesson.

Lessons

Each chapter contains six weeks' of lessons, each week contains three lessons. At the start of each half term there is an introductory lesson revisiting relevant content from work in previous years then introducing the new area of study. There is also a checkpoint section to check on the children's knowledge before proceeding to the next lesson.

All lessons including the introductory lesson have lesson plans that include the relevant combination of headings from below.

- **Lesson objectives:** A list of objectives for the lesson.
- **Resources:** What you require to teach the lesson.
- **Speaking scientifically:** A list of words to use in the lesson. The children should learn to spell them, understand their meanings and use them when talking about their activities, particularly when working scientifically.
- **Introduction:** A short and engaging activity to begin the lesson.
- **Whole-class work:** Working together as a class.

- **Group/Paired/Independent work:** Children working independently of the teacher in pairs, groups or alone.
- **Differentiation:** Ideas for how to support children who are struggling with a concept or how to extend those children who understand a concept without taking them onto new work.
- **Science in the wider world:** The information in this section may develop some of the content and concepts in the lesson and show how they relate to the wider world in their implications for humanity (such as health care) or impact on the environment (such as initiating conservation strategies).
- **Review:** A chance to review the children's learning and ensure the outcomes of the lesson have been achieved.

Assess and review

At the end of each chapter are activities for assessing and reviewing the children's understanding. These can be conducted during the course of the chapter's work, saved until the end of the chapter or done at a later date.

All assessment and review activities follow the same format:

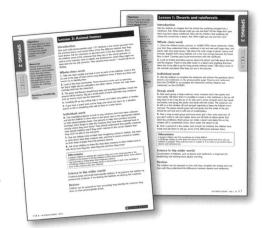

- **Curriculum objectives:** These are the areas of focus for the assess and review activity. There may be one focus or more than one depending on the activity.
- **Resources:** What you require to conduct the activities.
- **Working scientifically:** Each activity features one or more of the Working scientifically objectives for assessment.
- **Revise:** A series of short activities or one longer activity to revise and consolidate the children's learning and ensure they understand the concept(s).
- **Assess:** An assessment activity to provide a chance for the children to demonstrate their understanding and for you to check this.
- **Further practice:** Ideas for further practice on the focus, whether children are insecure in their learning or you want to provide extra practice or challenge.

Photocopiable pages

At the end of each chapter are some photocopiable pages that will have been referred to in the lesson plans.

These sheets are for the children to use; there is generally a title, an instruction, an activity and an 'I can' statement at the bottom. These sheets are also provided on the CD-ROM alongside additional pages as referenced in the lessons (see page 7 About the CD-ROM). The children should be encouraged to complete the 'I can' statements by colouring in the traffic lights to say how they think they have done (red – not very well, amber – ok, green – very well).

■SCHOLASTIC

About the CD-ROM

The CD-ROM contains:
- Printable versions of the photocopiable sheets from the book and additional photocopiable sheets as referenced in the lesson plans.
- Interactive activities for children to complete or to use on the whiteboard.
- Media resources to display.
- Printable versions of the lesson plans.
- Digital versions of the lesson plans with the relevant resources linked to them.

Getting started
- Put the CD-ROM into your CD-ROM drive.
  - For Windows users, the install wizard should autorun, if it fails to do so then navigate to your CD-ROM drive. Then follow the installation process.
  - For Mac users, copy the disk image file to your hard drive. After it has finished copying double-click it to mount the disk image. Navigate to the mounted disk image and run the installer. After installation the disk image can be unmounted and the DMG can be deleted from the hard drive.
- To complete the installation of the program you need to open the program and click 'Update' in the pop-up. Please note – this CD-ROM is web-enabled and the content will be downloaded from the internet to your hard-drive to populate the CD-ROM with the relevant resources. This only needs to be done on first use, after this you will be able to use the CD-ROM without an internet connection. If at any point any content is updated you will receive another pop-up upon start up with an internet connection.

Navigating the CD-ROM
There are two options to navigate the CD-ROM either as a Child or as a Teacher.

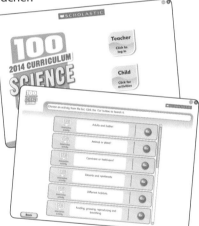

Child
- Click on the 'Child' button on the first menu screen.
- In the second menu click on the relevant class (please note only the books installed on the machine or network will be accessible. You can also rename year groups to match your school's naming conventions via the Teacher > Settings > Rename books area).
- A list of interactive activities will be displayed, children need to locate the correct one and click 'Go' to launch it.
- There is the opportunity to print or save a PDF of the activity at the end.

Teacher
- Click on the 'Teacher' button on the first menu screen and you will be taken to a screen showing which of the 100 English books you have purchased. From here, you can also access information about getting started and the credits.
- To enter the product click 'Next' in the bottom right.
- You then need to enter a password (the password is: login).
- On first use:
  - Enter as a Guest by clicking on the 'Guest' button.
  - If desired, create a profile for yourself by adding your name to the list of users. Profiles allow you to save favourites and to specify which year group(s) you wish to be able to view.
  - Go to 'Settings' to create a profile for yourself – click 'Add user' and enter your name. Then choose the year groups you wish to have access to (you can return to this screen to change this at any time). Click on 'Login' at the top of the screen to re-enter the disk under your new profile.
- On subsequent uses you can choose your name from the drop-down list. The 'Guest' option will always be available if you, or a colleague, wish to use this.
- You can search the CD-ROM using the tools or save favourites.

For more information about how to use the CD-ROM, please refer to the help file which can be found in the teacher area of the CD-ROM. It is a red button with a question mark on it on the right-hand side of the screen just underneath the 'Settings' tab.

Curriculum grid

The tables below show the weekly curriculum coverage for each chapter.

Curriculum objectives	Autumn 1						Autumn 2					
	W1	W2	W3	W4	W5	W6	W1	W2	W3	W4	W5	W6
Plants												
To observe and describe how seeds and bulbs grow into mature plants												
To find out and describe how plants need water, light and a suitable temperature to grow and stay healthy												
Animals, including humans												
To notice that animals, including humans, have offspring which grow into adults			✓				✓	✓	✓			
To find out about and describe the basic needs of animals, including humans, for survival (water, food, air)	✓			✓	✓	✓			✓	✓		
To describe the importance for humans of exercise, eating the right amounts of different types of food, and hygiene					✓	✓				✓	✓	✓
Everyday materials												
To identify and compare the uses of a variety of everyday materials, including wood, metal, plastic, glass, brick, rock, paper and cardboard for particular uses												
To find out how the shapes of solid objects made from some materials can be changed by squashing, bending, twisting and stretching												
Living things and their habitats												
To explore and compare the differences between things that are living, dead, and things that have never been alive		✓	✓	✓								
To identify that most living things live in habitats to which they are suited and describe how different habitats provide for the basic needs of different kinds of animals and plants, and how they depend on each other												
To identify and name a variety of plants and animals in their habitats and micro-habitats												
To describe how animals obtain their food from plants and other animals, using the idea of a simple food chain, and identify and name different sources of food												

Curriculum objectives	Spring 1						Spring 2					
	W1	W2	W3	W4	W5	W6	W1	W2	W3	W4	W5	W6
Plants												
To observe and describe how seeds and bulbs grow into mature plants	✓	✓			✓							
To find out and describe how plants need water, light and a suitable temperature to grow and stay healthy	✓		✓	✓	✓							✓
Animals, including humans												
To notice that animals, including humans, have offspring which grow into adults												
To find out about and describe the basic needs of animals, including humans, for survival (water, food, air)												
To describe the importance for humans of exercise, eating the right amounts of different types of food, and hygiene												
Everyday materials												
To identify and compare the uses of a variety of everyday materials, including wood, metal, plastic, glass, brick, rock, paper and cardboard for particular uses												
To find out how the shapes of solid objects made from some materials can be changed by squashing, bending, twisting and stretching												
Living things and their habitats												
To explore and compare the differences between things that are living, dead, and things that have never been alive												
To identify that most living things live in habitats to which they are suited and describe how different habitats provide for the basic needs of different kinds of animals and plants, and how they depend on each other	✓		✓	✓			✓		✓	✓		✓
To identify and name a variety of plants and animals in their habitats and micro-habitats		✓	✓		✓		✓	✓				
To describe how animals obtain their food from plants and other animals, using the idea of a simple food chain, and identify and name different sources of food					✓						✓	

Curriculum objectives	Summer 1						Summer 2					
	W1	W2	W3	W4	W5	W6	W1	W2	W3	W4	W5	W6
Plants												
To observe and describe how seeds and bulbs grow into mature plants												
To find out and describe how plants need water, light and a suitable temperature to grow and stay healthy												
Animals, including humans												
To notice that animals, including humans, have offspring which grow into adults												
To find out about and describe the basic needs of animals, including humans, for survival (water, food, air)												
To describe the importance for humans of exercise, eating the right amounts of different types of food, and hygiene												
Everyday materials												
To identify and compare the uses of a variety of everyday materials, including wood, metal, plastic, glass, brick, rock, paper and cardboard for particular uses	✓	✓	✓	✓	✓	✓	✓		✓			
To find out how the shapes of solid objects made from some materials can be changed by squashing, bending, twisting and stretching					✓	✓	✓	✓				
Living things and their habitats												
To explore and compare the differences between things that are living, dead, and things that have never been alive												
To identify that most living things live in habitats to which they are suited and describe how different habitats provide for the basic needs of different kinds of animals and plants, and how they depend on each other												
To identify and name a variety of plants and animals in their habitats and micro-habitats												
To describe how animals obtain their food from plants and other animals, using the idea of a simple food chain, and identify and name different sources of food												

All living things

Expected prior learning

- Can identify the basic parts of the human body.
- Know types of living creatures, such as mammals, insects, reptiles and amphibians.
- Know the names of some mammals, insects, birds and so on.
- Know the names of simple parts of plants.
- Understand what our senses are, how we use them and what part of the body we use for each sense.

Overview of progression

After completing this chapter they should know about the:

- characteristics of being human
- characteristics of all living things
- differences between living things and things that have never been alive
- differences between dead things and those that have never been alive
- differences between living things such as plants and animals
- characteristics that are essential for keeping us alive.

Creative context

- This chapter provides opportunities for children to make observational drawings and to use different visual images to illustrate their findings. There are also opportunities in art to paint and produce leaf rubbings.

Background knowledge

Animals and plants have many similarities as well as differences. Animals are, of course, mobile and plants aren't but plants do actually move as they grow and some flowers even turn towards the sun. Children may say that animals breathe and plants do not; plants do need to take in air but they do not breathe in and out visibly as mammals do.

Speaking scientifically

- You may wish the children to know the names of more detailed parts of living things including joints, such as ankles and knees in humans; beaks and feathers in birds; and antennae in insects.
- They will also need to be familiar with terms such as 'weight' and 'weigh', 'measure', 'height' and 'similar' and 'different'.

Preparation

You will need to provide: good quality paper for drawing; 1 cm-squared paper; string; measuring tapes; bathroom scales; magnifying lenses; living plants and any animals kept at school; sugar; crisps; an onion; ice; ink pad; pictures of humans of all ages; 3 poems or nursery rhymes; cress, grass and marigold seeds; seed trays; seed compost; small trowels or tablespoons; a selection of wooden objects; a selection of dry foods; a selection of metal and plastic objects; examples of the children's own toys; a wide range of pictures and DVDs of animals, birds and insects; a range of objects for display and classification that are either 'dead' or have 'never been alive'.

On the CD-ROM you will find: photocopiable pages 'Parts of the body', 'Toys and food'; interactive activities 'Feeding, growing, reproducing and breathing', 'Adults and babies', 'Carnivore or herbivore?', 'Senses'; media resources 'Parts of a flower (1)', 'What do these animals do?'

Chapter at a glance

Week	Lesson	Curriculum objectives	Objectives	Main activity	Working scientifically
1	1	• *To revise the objectives of Year I.* • *To identify, name, draw and label the basic parts of the human body.*	• To introduce the idea that we each have individual characteristics.	Understanding names for parts of the body and labelling a diagram of the human body. Introducing physical characteristics such as hair colour, eye colour, how tall, number of legs.	• Using their observations and ideas to suggest answers to questions.
	2	• *To be introduced to the idea that all living things have certain characteristics that are essential for keeping them alive and healthy.*	• To consider the differences between living things (humans).	Labelling and colouring a diagram of the human face with a friend's hair/eye colour etc. Comparing each other's height and weight.	• Observing closely • Gathering and recording data.
	3	• *To be introduced to the idea that all living things have certain characteristics that are essential for keeping them alive and healthy.*	• To understand their own bodies and to compare characteristics.	Measuring hand size and hand span. Looking at fingerprints.	• Gathering and recording data to help answer questions.
2	1	• To explore the differences between things that are living and things that have never been alive.	• To understand the differences between things that are living and things that are not living.	Working individually and in groups to identify what is living and not living from a range of pictures and objects.	• Identifying and classifying. • Comparing simple features of objects and deciding how to sort and group them.
	2	• To explore and compare the differences between things that are dead and things that have never been alive.	• To understand what it means to be alive.	Asking and answering questions about different plants, animals, and objects that are not alive.	• Using their observations and ideas to suggest answers to questions.
	3	• To explore and compare the differences between things that are dead and things that have never been alive.	• To understand and identify the differences between 'dead' and 'never been alive'.	Going on a treasure hunt to find objects that are dead or have never been alive. Sorting objects into 'dead' and 'never been alive'.	• Gathering and recording data to help answer questions. • Identifying and classifying.
3	1	• To explore and compare the differences between things that are dead and things that have never been alive.	• To understand and identify the differences between 'living', 'dead' and 'never been alive'.	Discussing the differences between 'alive', 'dead' and 'never been alive'. Highlighting words in nursery rhymes according to whether they are dead, alive or have never been alive.	• Identifying and classifying.
	2	• *To become familiar with the life processes that are common to all living things.*	• To understand the similarities and differences between mammals – including humans. • To understand that all animals, including humans, grow and change.	Using pictures of different animals for discussion. Completing sentences/drawings /an interactive activity relating to characteristics of mammals.	• Identifying and classifying.
	3	• *To become familiar with the life processes that are common to all living things.*	• To understand that living things change throughout their lives.	Discussing humans – from being a baby to old age.	• Using their observations and ideas to suggest answers to questions.

Chapter at a glance

Week	Lesson	Curriculum objectives	Objectives	Main activity	Working scientifically
4	1	• To explore and compare the differences between things that are dead and things that have never been alive.	• To understand that there are differences between living things. • To be able to sort living things into groups.	Using pictures of different living things: humans, mammals, birds, insects and so on. Completing a differences chart.	• Identifying and classifying. • Using their observations and ideas to suggest answers to questions.
	2	• To be introduced to the idea that all living things have certain characteristics that are essential for keeping them alive and healthy.	• To be able to identify different parts of a plant.	Discussing a range of plants and their parts. Individual drawings and leaf rubbings.	• Understanding similarities and differences. • Using their observations and ideas to suggest answers to questions.
	3	• To be introduced to the idea that all living things have certain characteristics that are essential for keeping them alive and healthy.	• To recognise the importance of seeds. • To understand how seeds grow.	Discussing the importance of seeds. Growing cress, marigolds and grass.	• Observing closely.
5	1	• To be introduced to the idea that all living things have certain characteristics that are essential for keeping them alive and healthy.	• To know what we need to stay alive and healthy.	Discussing our needs and how we achieve them. Drawing pictures and completing sentences to compare our needs in hot and cold climates.	• Make comparisons between simple features of objects, materials and living things.
	2	• To be introduced to the idea that all living things have certain characteristics that are essential for keeping them alive and healthy.	• To know what it is that makes us human and different from other living things.	Discussing differences between us and other living things. Group work comparing people and dogs.	• Understanding similarities and differences. • • Answering simple questions.
	3	• To be introduced to the idea that all living things have certain characteristics that are essential for keeping them alive and healthy.	• To recognise and understand some differences between mammals.	Discussing mammals such as dogs, lions, cows, and zebras and classifying them into herbivores and carnivores. Matching pictures to types of mammal.	• Identifying and classifying.
6	1	• To become familiar with the life processes that are common to all living things.	• To understand what it means to be healthy.	Discussing and listing things that help us to stay healthy: exercise, the right food, using medicines and curing illness.	• Using their observations and ideas to suggest answers to questions.
	2	• To be introduced to the idea that all living things have certain characteristics that are essential for keeping them alive and healthy.	• To know what our senses are, how essential they are and how we use them.	Examining senses. Using different senses to identify different foods.	• Performing simple tests.
	3	• To be introduced to the idea that all living things have certain characteristics that are essential for keeping them alive and healthy.	• To understand the importance of senses to different animals.	Identifying similarities and differences in how different creatures use their senses.	• Using their observations and ideas to suggest answers to questions.
Assess and review					

Objectives
● To introduce the idea that we each have individual characteristics.

Resources
A large picture of a child or adult; a large piece of paper; photocopiable page 36 'The human face'; words for parts of the body either as individual sheets or displayed on the classroom wall

Speaking scientifically
parts of the body: arms, legs, head, mouth, ankle, knee, elbow and so on; the same, different

Lesson 1: Recognising and identifying 'me'

Previous knowledge
The children should know the names of a variety of common plants and animals including mammals, insects, reptiles and so on. They should have also looked at the human body in earlier years, from which they should already know the names of the basic body parts.

Introduction
Explain to the class that you will be starting a new topic on all living things and you want to find out what they already know about themselves and their bodies.

Ask two boys to come to the front of the class and ask the children the following two questions: *How are they similar? How are they different?* Do the same with two girls and then a boy and a girl. Talk about their observations, making sure that the children notice similarities such as two arms, two legs, one head, one mouth and so on, but that they also point out differences such as hair, eye colour, height and so on.

Whole-class work
1. Ask a child to walk across the room and discuss the parts of their body that they are using, making sure that their observations are as detailed as possible and include references to toes, feet, legs, knee joints and possibly hip joints.

2. Repeat this by asking a child to pick up an object, (which requires fingers, hands, wrists, elbows and so on), eat a biscuit (requiring their mouth, lips, jaw and head) and bend down (using their feet, legs, waist, back and so on).

3. Write as many of the words used as you can on the whiteboard.

4. During the discussion emphasise that we all use the same parts of our bodies for the same actions.

Group work
5. Give each group a large piece of paper and ask one person to write down each of these parts of the body: mouth, legs, arms, hands, spine/backbone. Alongside each part of the body, different children in the group can draw what we actually use it for.

6. Each child needs to use photocopiable page 36 'The human face'. Tell them to label it accurately with as many parts as they can. When they label the hair and eyes they should colour them in using their own hair and eye colour.

Introducing the new area of study
Challenge the children to work in pairs and to think of four parts of their body: for example, hand, foot, head and mouth. They should explore the different ways that each part is used. They could show their partners various ways of using each part. For example, we use our mouths to smile, to talk, to eat; we use our hands to wave, to hold something, and to fasten buttons. Ask: *What do we actually use joints such as wrists and elbows for? What do we use our little fingers for?*

It is important to realise that as living animals we do have two legs, two arms, two eyes and so on and that in some ways we are the same as all our friends, but we are also different: some people are taller than other people; some friends might have darker hair or different coloured eyes.

> ### Differentiation
> ● Support children with the wide range of names for parts of the body. In the group work, some children will need support to match body parts to how they are used.
> ● Challenge children to find out what are the most common hair and eye colours in the class and to show this by using a simple bar graph.

Checkpoint
- Can you name an animal with wings/feathers/four legs/a tail?
- Can you name a mammal/bird/fish/reptile/amphibian/invertebrate?
- How many different body parts can you name?
- What are the five senses?
- Which sense do we use our ears/eyes/nose/tongue/hands for?

Science in the wider world
We all use our legs, feet, joints and so on to run, but athletes train and practise to make sure that they run faster.

Review
The children could be assessed on how accurate they are in labelling body parts and in how many answers they can give to questions such as: *How many uses are there for our arms/legs/hands?*

Objectives
● To consider the differences between living things (humans).

Resources
Photocopiable page 36 'The human face'; several bathroom scales (preferably one per pair); rulers and measuring tapes/sticks for height (preferably one of each for each pair of children); large and small sheets of paper

Speaking scientifically
height, weight, the same, different, similar

Lesson 2: Differences between friends

Introduction

Remind the children about the similarities between people (two arms, two legs, one mouth, one nose and so on) and the differences (hair colour, eye colour, gender and so on). Introduce the idea that height and weight can also be different.

Whole-class work

I. Discuss how we know whether someone is taller, shorter, heavier or lighter than we are. (Be aware that some children may be sensitive about their height and/or weight.)

2. Measure some children and mark their heights to illustrate the differences.

3. Explain how to use the scales for measuring weight.

Paired work

4. Let the children work in pairs and use a clean photocopiable page 36 'The human face' to mark each other's hair and eye colour and compare the differences.

5. In pairs, the children should write each of their names on a sheet of paper. Ask them to use the scales to weigh each other and then use the measuring tape to measure each other's height. (Note: sensitivity may be required regarding this exercise and parental permission may need to be sought.)

6. The children should record their data on the sheet of paper. This piece of paper needs to be kept safe for lesson 3.

Differentiation
● Support children when asking each other questions and identifying differences.
● Support children in measuring height and weight.

Science in the wider world

An understanding of the meaning of 'similar', 'same' and 'different' and how to collect evidence and compare two things is important in all kinds of contexts. This will apply to many of the areas of study that the children will be completing in Year 2, for example, similarities and differences between mammals and/or birds, or how we know what materials something is made of, or comparing habitats.

Review

Consider the accuracy of the children's measurements and observations and ask them to check that the eye and hair colour used on their photocopiable sheet is correct.

Objectives
● To understand their own bodies and to compare characteristics.

Resources
The paper from lesson 2 that recorded their height and weight; more sheets of plain paper; sheets of 1cm-squared paper (the paper should be high quality so that it can be used as part of a classroom display); an ink pad for recording fingerprints; string; rulers; magnifying lenses; a whole-class fingerprint grid with each child's name alongside a space to record their fingerprints

Speaking scientifically
span, fingerprint, different, bigger, smaller

Lesson 3: Measuring myself

Introduction
Ask the class the following questions, which could be written on the whiteboard and used as another example of how to record data: *Who do you think is the tallest/smallest person in the class? Who do you think is the heaviest/lightest person in the class?* (This may be a sensitive issue, even at this young age and it is important to understand that some children may be self-conscious about their weight. You may want to allow children to opt out of this part of the activity.) Use the sheets with the heights and weights of each child from the previous lesson to find out the accurate answers. Discuss the results to review the previous work on similarities and differences.

Whole-class work
1. Remind the children of the differences that they have already found and discuss how they have written down their measurements and recorded them. They should have their completed photocopiable page 36 'The human face' and the paper with their height and weight and the height and weight of their friend. Explain that they will now be measuring their spans, the size of their hands and taking their fingerprints.

2. Use your own hand to show the whole class how to measure their span by using a piece of string and then a ruler.

3. Use your own hand and draw round it on a piece of squared paper. Show the class how to count the squares and possibly half squares to find the size.

Paired work
4. The children should work in pairs to help each other measure their spans and hand size. It is important that they label their pieces of paper clearly with their names.

5. After the group work it is important to use the data and all the measurements to discuss the similarities and differences, and to use the information as part of a classroom display.

6. The data on eye and hair colour can be used to construct bar charts as another way to record data.

7. When they are measuring, take the children's fingerprints and record them on the prepared chart (classroom assistants may be required to help with this).

8. The magnifying lenses can be used to look closely at individual fingerprints. The children can then try to draw the patterns on larger pieces of paper. These will be almost like abstract doodles and could be part of a much longer art lesson.

Differentiation
● Support children who find measuring difficult and, if necessary, help them to measure so that they get accurate data.
● Challenge children to rank the class in order of height, span length, hand size and so on, and to look at secondary sources for more information on fingerprints.

Science in the wider world
Fingerprints are used by police all over the world to catch criminals because each of us has a unique print.

Review
The children could be assessed on how accurate their measurements are when they use their rulers and how carefully they have recorded the data in different ways.

Objectives
● To understand the differences between things that are living and things that are not living.

Resources
Photocopiable page 37 'Living and not living'; pictures of living things, including animals and plants; a range of plants in pots and vases; if possible, any animals that are kept in the school; access to the school grounds

Speaking scientifically
breathing, plant, eating, animal, mammal, insect, bird, reptile, similar, different, living, not living

Lesson 1: What do 'living' and 'not living' mean?

Introduction
Ask the children to look round the classroom and write down everything they can see that is living and everything that is not living. If possible, take them around the school and part of the grounds so that they can add many things to their lists. It is important to make sure that the children understand that 'living' applies to plants as well animals and that objects that aren't alive include things made of wood, as well as dead leaves and twigs.

Whole-class work
1. Discuss the lists that they have made by asking individuals to name something in the classroom or from around the school that is alive and something that is not alive. Make a whole-class list on the whiteboard.

2. When the whole class is together, ask them to look at each other, to look at you and to look at themselves. Ask: *What are you actually doing now?*

3. Lead the discussion away from answers such as 'sitting down' or 'sitting in the classroom' towards answers that suggest what it means to be alive.

4. As soon as you get answers such as breathing, moving, thinking, talking and so on, write them down where the whole class can see them. Explain that these are characteristics of being alive.

5. Ask: *What will you be doing at lunchtime? What will you be doing during the night?* Write down the answers, such as eating, drinking and sleeping. Explain that these are also characteristics of being alive.

Paired/individual work
6. Ask the children to work in pairs to discuss and then complete photocopiable page 37 'Living and not living'.

7. Ask them to work on their own to complete the sentences below, which require them to compare living and non-living things; using the words that are characteristics of being alive. Tell them to try to use as many different words as possible.

- The butterfly is alive because it _____.
- The plant is alive because it _____.
- My goldfish is alive because _____.
- The motorbike is not alive because _____.
- The cup and saucer are not alive because _____.
- I am alive because I can _____.

Differentiation
● Support children who need help understanding the photocopiable sheet and some of the more difficult words that have been written for them to use. Some of the spellings may be difficult.
● Encourage children to begin to think about the wide variety of things that are living and perhaps link as many characteristics of a living plant and themselves.

Science in the wider world
By understanding the characteristics of being alive (eating, drinking, breathing and so on), it should be possible to begin to move towards much broader ideas about habitat conservation and global warming.

Review
The most important issues in this lesson that need to be reviewed and consolidated are the characteristics of being alive and the wide range of living things.

Objectives
● To understand what it means to be alive.

Resources
Photocopiable page 38 'Feeding, growing, reproducing and breathing' or interactive activity 'Feeding, growing, reproducing and breathing' on the CD-ROM; objects or pictures of the objects from the photocopiable sheet (optional)

Speaking scientifically
living, not living, reproducing, feeding, growing, moving

Lesson 2: Signs of life

Introduction

Discuss with the whole class what it means to be alive – to be a living creature. Ask: *How do you know that you are alive?* During the discussion make sure that the answers include: breathing, growing, moving, feeding/eating and reproducing/having babies.

Refer to objects around the classroom and outside to remind the children of the difference between things that are living and not living. This is also an opportunity to find out how much the children know about the wide range of living things. It will be useful for future chapters to introduce or to begin to consolidate distinctions between mammals, birds, reptiles, insects, amphibians, invertebrates and so on.

Whole-class work

1. Follow up the introduction by asking three more questions and discussing the children's answers: *How can you tell that a mouse is living? How can you tell that a butterfly is living? How can you tell that a snake is living?*

2. Write down where the children can see them the words breathe, grow, breed and move, and discuss what these mean.

Group work

3. Give each child photocopiable page 38 'Feeding, growing, reproducing and breathing' or the interactive activity 'Feeding, growing, reproducing and breathing' on the CD-ROM.

4. Ask them to look at the first box headed 'Which of these feed?' and go through each example by reading the word and looking at each picture (crocodile, rock, sand, mushroom). If possible, give them a piece of rock or a mushroom to hold.

5. Ask them to use their observations to complete the other three boxes, which ask the children to identify which objects grow, reproduce and breathe. They should talk about their answers with their group. If possible, have pictures or real objects available.

6. After they have completed the photocopiable sheet in their groups it is important to discuss their answers by asking questions such as: *How do you know that a sparrow moves? How does it move? How does a dandelion reproduce? Why can't a tin can move? Why doesn't an iron nail grow?*

Differentiation
● Support children during the group work when they are trying to identify the characteristics of living things: help them to understand the terms 'feed', 'grow', 'move' and so on.
● Challenge children to explain how plants reproduce, how trees grow and how mushrooms and other plants feed.

Science in the wider world

Understanding the basic needs of living things will help us to understand how we can maintain their environments. For example, we need to make sure that living things have food, and space to grow and move around.

Review

The children can be assessed on their understanding of what it means to be alive. Sit with them during the group work to assess their understanding of this.

Objectives
• To understand and identify the differences between 'dead' and 'never been alive'.

Resources
Children will need to use the classroom and the school grounds; objects and materials such as rock, sand, flour, dead twigs and leaves; rubber; plastic bottles; paintbrushes; metal objects; woollen and cotton material; a medium-sized piece of paper for each group with two headings 'Never been alive' and 'Dead' (or if you prefer 'No longer alive'); coloured pencils

Speaking scientifically
living, dead, never been alive, no longer alive

Lesson 3: 'Dead' and 'never been alive'

Introduction
Remind the children of the characteristics of living things and revisit some of the animals and plants that breathe, grow, feed and move. Develop the discussion from 'alive' through to 'no longer alive', or dead. This may well be a sensitive issue so has to be handled carefully. The idea is probably best discussed in the abstract without using specific examples that they might relate to their family or to their pets. If alive means eating, moving, breathing, breeding and so on, being dead means the opposite – no longer eating, breathing, or moving and so on. In terms of plants, it is possible to see dead twigs and leaves and there may be empty snail's shells available.

Whole-class work
1. Before the lesson starts, prepare for a treasure hunt by arranging some of the objects you want to be found in various places in the classroom and around the school. These should include plastics, rocks, paper, sand, metal objects, things made of rubber, dead twigs and leaves, pine cones, snail shells and so on.

2. Explain to the whole class that they will be going on a treasure hunt to collect objects that are either dead or have never been alive. It might be a good idea not to be any more specific than that – but it might be useful to explain that they must not collect anything that is alive (breathes, eats, breeds and moves).

Group work
3. Allow the children to spend 15 minutes in small groups collecting their objects from inside the classroom or outside in the school grounds.

4. When they come back into the classroom ask them to arrange their objects into two piles: 'dead' – or if you prefer 'no longer alive', and 'never been alive'.

5. After the whole-class discussion give each group the sheet of paper with the headings, 'Never been alive' and 'No longer alive', to record their data.

6. Ask each group to write down the name of each object in the correct column. They could also draw some of the objects and use the sheets to display what they have found out.

> **Differentiation**
> • Support children who might find the concepts difficult, especially in placing the objects in the right pile or column on the sheet of paper.
> • Challenge children to explain their choices in more detail by asking them questions like: *Why is paper in the column 'No longer alive'? What is flour? Why has plastic never been alive?* (However, the children may be interested to know that plastic is made from oil, which is formed from the decomposed bodies of ancient tiny sea creatures. So, technically, could be said to have once been alive!)

Science in the wider world
Many of the things we take for granted such as food, rubber and paper are made from living things, so it is important that we look after the plants that they are made from.

Review
The children need to be clear what the objects that are no longer alive have in common and similarly what those that have never been alive have in common.

Objectives
● To understand and identify the differences between 'living', 'dead' and 'never been alive'.

Resources
Individual copies of three poems or nursery rhymes printed with large fonts (for example, 'Hey diddle diddle', 'Humpty Dumpty' and 'The owl and the pussycat'), yellow, red and green highlighters

Speaking scientifically
living, dead, never been alive, feeding, growing, moving, breathing, breeding

Lesson 1: Identifying 'living', 'dead' and 'never been alive'

Introduction
Use the first part of the lesson to consolidate the children's previous knowledge. Ask: *How do you know that you are alive?* Show them a pot plant and ask: *How do you know that this is alive?* Show them a dead twig and their wooden desk. Ask: *How do you know that these were once alive?* Show them something made of plastic or the glass window. Ask: *How do you know that this has never been alive?*

Whole-class work
1. Tell them that you are going to try to find out whether they have understood what 'living', 'dead' (no longer alive) and 'never been alive' mean.

2. Discuss each of the three definitions briefly.

3. Provide each child with a copy of the nursery rhymes and read them together.

Individual work
4. Give the children the sheets with the poems on and three coloured pens or highlighters.

5. Ask them to highlight or underline all the animals or objects: green if it is alive; red if it is dead; yellow if it has never been alive.

6. Discuss with the class how they have sorted the objects and consolidate their understanding of all the terms that have been used.

> ### Differentiation
> ● Support children if they need help to find which animals or objects to highlight. Some children may also need help with reading the poems.
> ● Challenge children to explain some of the more difficult words such as 'honey' and 'money' in 'The owl and the pussycat' and ask them to justify their answers.

Science in the wider world
It is important to reinforce what plants and animals need in order to survive and grow – food, shelter and so on. Understanding their needs will lead to children being more aware of conservation.

Review
This lesson is about consolidating the children's knowledge and they need to be assessed on their understanding of the three terms that they have been using: 'alive', 'dead' and 'never been alive'.

When considering 'never been alive' some of the children will be aware of the processes needed to change a living thing, such as a tree, into dead materials, such as paper, as well as the process of changing a rock that has never been alive into a metal jug that has also never been alive.

Objectives
• To understand the similarities and differences between mammals – including humans.
• To understand that all animals, including humans, grow and change.

Resources
Photocopiable page 39 'Animals and their young'; interactive activity 'Adults and babies' on the CD-ROM'; photographs, posters, DVDs and so on of different kinds of mammal; art paper; coloured pencils; crayons; felt-tipped pens

Speaking scientifically
baby, adult, mammal

Lesson 2: Characteristics of mammals

Introduction
Prepare the classroom by displaying as many pictures of mammals as you can and have a large picture of a person at the front of the classroom. Remind the children that the person is a human just like they are and ask them what humans can do. The answers should include simple things such as run, walk, see, hear, eat and breathe. It is important to make sure that the children also understand that humans are warm-blooded, have live babies and are able to feed them. Explain that this lesson is about creatures called mammals.

Whole-class work
1. Explain to the children that they and all humans are mammals. Show them the pictures of mammals on the walls and as you point to each one ask them to name it. It is important to use a range of mammals.

2. Ask them to describe some of the similarities and differences. It is important that the children understand the wide range of different types of mammal.

3. Complete interactive activity 'Adults and babies' on the CD-ROM as a whole-class activity. Emphasise that all living things, including humans, grow.

Individual work
4. Give each child photocopiable page 39 'Animals and their young' to complete.

5. Give each child a piece of art paper and ask them to draw their favourite mammal.

6. Underneath their drawings they should complete the following sentences to explain why their animal can be classified as a mammal:
  • I am a _____ and I am a mammal.
  • This is what I can do: _____ and _____ and
    _____.

7. The drawings can be part of a 'Mammals' display or part of a wider display on all living things.

Differentiation
• Support children who need help explaining what the characteristics of being a mammal are. Support children who need help in completing the sentences and the captions underneath their pictures
• Challenge the children to find out about unusual mammals such as kangaroos and whales and encourage them to explain why they are unusual to the rest of the class.

Science in the wider world
Mammals are the dominant life form and many, such as apes, are very similar to us. Understanding more about mammals should eventually help children to develop their own views on conservation and what we can do to support mammals in the wild.

Review
The children could be assessed on how many mammals they can recognise and what they understand about how mammals are different from other creatures such as birds.

Objectives
● To understand that living things change throughout their lives.

Resources
Photographs and posters of babies, children their age, adults and grandparents; large pieces of paper

Speaking scientifically
growing, changing, bigger, stronger

Lesson 3: Changes to living things

Introduction
Use the pictures of babies, children and adults to explain to the children that mammals, including humans, grow and change during their lives and as they get older.

Whole-class work
1. Discuss with the children some of the changes that have already taken place from when they were babies to the age that they are now. These should include being able to walk and talk, growing bigger and getting stronger.

2. Ask them how they think they will change between now and when they are adults.

3. Use examples from other mammals such as elephants and their own pets such as cats and dogs. What differences can they observe between baby animals and adult ones?

4. Explain that all mammal babies need help from adults. Ask: *What do mother cats do to help their kittens?* Their answers should include: feed them, keep them warm, keep them safe, and teach them how to behave. Ask: *How is this the same as, or different from, how your parents help you?*

Paired work
5. Ask the children to work in pairs to complete the statements below on the large piece of paper. Each of their answers could be illustrated with drawings.

● When I was a baby I could _____.
● Now I can _____.
● When I was a baby an adult had to help me by _____.
● When I become an adult I will be able to _____.

Differentiation
● Support children in understanding the main differences between babies and adults and the vocabulary needed to complete their statements on the large sheet of paper.
● Challenge children to think about other creatures that change, such as butterflies and other insects, and how these changes are different from changes in humans.

Science in the wider world
This lesson looks briefly at the idea of dependence. This links to other areas of dependence, such as humans and food supplies, mammals and their sources of food, and humans and energy needs.

Review
Children should be assessed on their understanding of changes in mammals from birth to adulthood and how these changes are similar and different in other mammals. They also need to understand that other creatures do change and grow during their lives but in many different ways.

Objectives
● To understand that there are differences between living things.
● To be able to sort living things into groups.

Resources
Pictures of a range of creatures displayed around the room or piles of magazines; coloured pencils; glue; scissors; a large sheet of display paper for each group

Speaking scientifically
backbone, plant, reptile, amphibian, mammal, insect, bird

Lesson 1: Differences between living things

Introduction

Explain to the children that they will be looking at and trying to describe many different types of creature. Create a table on the whiteboard with the following headings: insects; reptiles; birds; mammals; plants; amphibians. Read the words and, if necessary, explain what they mean. Point to a picture on one of the tables, or displayed around the room, and ask which column to put it in. Write it in the column and go on to the next one. There should be several names written in each column.

Whole-class work

1. Look at each column on the board in turn and discuss how the children would describe the creatures that have been written down. Use questions and statements, including: *Describe an insect. How is a flying insect different from a bird? Do all plants have easily seen flowers? What can birds do that we can't? What is special about amphibians? Are all reptiles amphibians?*

2. Ask them to tell you three or four more names of plants or creatures for each of the columns.

3. Talk about other ways of grouping some of the animals in your columns such as: those with fur; those with feathers; those that can fly; those with backbones.

Group work

4. Write the following headings on the whiteboard: 'Creatures with fur'; 'Creatures with scales'; 'Creatures with backbones'; 'Creatures that fly'.

5. Ask the children to work in groups of four to find creatures in the magazines and piles of pictures that fit under each heading.

6. Creatures that fly, for example, could include butterflies, dragonflies and various birds; creatures with scales will include snakes and lizards.

7. When they have collected the pictures ask them whether it is possible to arrange them into different piles. Ask: *Do creatures that fly also have backbones? Do creatures with scales have backbones?*

8. You could create a class display under the same headings: each group could draw animals for one specific heading, or cut them out and stick them onto card.

> **Differentiation**
> ● Support the children with vocabulary such as 'amphibian' and 'reptile'. Some children will also need support when they are deciding under which heading to place the various creatures and plants.
> ● Challenge children to place plants in various categories, such as trees, ferns, flowering plants and grasses.

Science in the wider world

Grouping items in terms of different criteria is common in science and is a very useful skill. Asking appropriate questions such as, 'Why is this plant or this creature in this group?' or 'What makes this creature or plant fit into this group?' is also a very useful skill.

Review

The children should be assessed on their understanding of how animals and plants can be grouped and their knowledge of the common characteristics of amphibians, birds, reptiles and insects.

Objectives
● To be able to identify different parts of a plant.

Resources
Media resource 'Parts of a flower (1)' on the CD-ROM; photocopiable page 40 'Parts of a plant'; rulers; coloured pencils; a selection of leaves (including large deciduous leaves); black wax crayons for leaf rubbing; access to the school grounds

Speaking scientifically
stem, root, flower, leaf, seed, similar, different

Lesson 2: What is a plant?

Introduction
Take the children out into the school grounds to look at a wide range of plants such as trees, bushes, flowers, grasses, moss and so on. Get them to touch the leaves and feel the grass and to look carefully at any seeds and fruits.

Whole-class work
1. Discuss with the children some of the common characteristics of plants and write their ideas on the whiteboard. Ensure sure they include such things as: most plants are green; they grow in the ground; they have leaves, roots and flowers. Use the diagram in media resource 'Parts of a flower (1)' on the CD-ROM to revise this.

2. Ask the children how they think plants are similar to us and different from us. Make sure that the discussion includes facts such as: plants and humans grow; plants can't walk or run but humans can; plants and humans both need food, water and light. Some of these similarities and differences only need to be mentioned briefly because they will be looked at again in later lessons.

3. Show the children some of the different leaves and ask them to think of words to describe them, such as pointed, spiny, small, large, and so on.

4. Give each group a selection of large leaves, art paper and black wax crayons.

5. Give each child photocopiable page 40 'Parts of a plant'.

Group work
6. Show the children that most of the leaves on their table have a rough side and a smooth side and that the veins carry food to the leaves. Remind them that all livings things need food to stay alive.

7. Ask them to choose a leaf each and rub it using the paper and wax crayon. These rubbings can be used as part of a plant display.

8. Quickly ask the whole class about the names for parts of plants – go over those parts that were discussed earlier.

9. Tell them to complete the photocopiable sheet, which requires them to match the names to the parts of the plant.

Differentiation
● Support children who are still not clear about the names of the different parts of a plant and who might have difficulty reading them on their photocopiable sheet.
● Challenge children to compare plants and humans and to write down a full list of similarities and differences.

Science in the wider world
One of the challenges facing children in the future will be conserving plants and animal life within a world where the climate is likely to change and the population will grow. The more they are aware of plants and their needs in terms of diversity and habitat, the more likely they are to face up to these challenges.

Review
The children need to know the names of parts of plants and could be assessed on how well they have completed the photocopiable sheet. They could also be assessed on how much they understand about the similarities and differences between plants and animals.

Objectives
• To recognise the importance of seeds.
• To understand how seeds grow.

Resources
Completed photocopiable sheets from the previous lesson; pictures of wheat or examples of stalks of wheat; cress, grass and marigold seeds; three small seed trays for each group; seed compost; small trowels or tablespoons

Speaking scientifically
seeds, germinate

Lesson 3: Seeds

Introduction
Discuss with the children the names for parts of a plant by using the labelled photocopiable page 40 'Parts of a plant' from the previous lesson. Explain to them where they would find the seeds on most plants. Show them what they have on their tables which will include paper and pencils, three seed trays, three small piles of labelled seeds (cress, grass and marigold) and small trowels or spoons. Explain to the class that plants grow and produce seeds which then grow into more plants and more seeds and so on.

Whole-class work
1. Discuss the importance of seeds by using wheat as an example. Tell the class what wheat is used for and that without flour they wouldn't have bread and sandwiches, pizzas or pasta.

2. Explain that rice is a very important crop and many people in the world eat a lot of rice.

3. Most cereal seeds such as rice and wheat are grasses. Discuss how important grasses are to wild animals such as deer, zebra and cattle – and how cows then provide us with milk, meat and cheese.

4. The children should have some understanding of how important it is for seeds to grow.

5. Discuss with them how seeds do actually grow. Make sure that they have some understanding of soil and water. There is no need at this stage to talk about their need for warmth and light, which will be taught in later lessons.

6. It is important to use the word 'germinate' so that they understand the change from seed to leaf and plant.

Group work
7. Explain to the children how to plant the three different seeds and then let them plant the seeds in the three trays. The label they write for each tray needs to say:
- Name of the seed: _____
- We planted the seed on _____ (date).
- It germinated on _____.

Make sure that each group has a daily watering schedule so that the seeds will grow. Their observations can be recorded on the label.

> ### Differentiation
> • Some children may need help when they are planting the seeds to make sure that they do not plant them too deeply.
> • Challenge children to make a list of different cereal crops and then to say why they are important.

Science in the wider world
We all need food, and cereal crops are vital for our survival. If we have good crops – in other words, if the seeds grow – we will have enough food. If they don't grow well there will be problems. It is important that children begin to realise the importance of seeds and food crops.

Review
The children should be assessed on their understanding of seeds and cereal crops and what they are used for, as well as their ability to grow seeds and record their results.

Lesson 1: Staying alive

Introduction

Ask the children what they had for breakfast and make a list of the different foods on the whiteboard. Ask them why they think that we need to eat and drink and what would happen to us if we didn't. Emphasise the idea that we need certain things, like food and drink, to help us to stay alive. Ask them what other things they think they might need to help them to stay alive. Write down their answers – and make sure that they include clothes and shelter.

Whole-class work

1. Tell the children how important it is for us to eat, drink and be protected from the weather.

2. Introduce them to two imaginary children – Charlotte and Charlie – and ask them to think what it would be like to live in a hot country. Discuss what the two children would need to live comfortably.

3. Ask them to imagine the same children living in a very cold country. Discuss what they would need to live comfortably.

4. During the discussions write any useful words or phrases on the whiteboard. Invite the children to make comparisons between what we need in a hot climate and what we need in a cold one.

Paired work

5. Ask the children to work in pairs and draw Charlie and Charlotte at the top of their large piece of paper. They will then need to write two headings: 'Cold places' and 'Hot places'.

6. Ask them to list what the two children will need to keep them alive and healthy under each of the two headings. They could also draw pictures.

7. Ask them to complete the following sentences about themselves at the bottom of their sheet of paper:

● I eat lots of _____ and _____ and _____.
● I drink lots of _____ and _____.
● My house shelters me because it has _____ and _____.

Differentiation
● Support children who need help with understanding some of the terms, such as 'shelter', 'protection' and so on. Some children will need help with spelling the words that are needed to complete the sentences on their sheets of paper.
● Challenge children to find out about specific people and what they need to stay healthy. For example, the Inuit live in very cold places, and some Africans (such as Bushmen) live in very hot conditions.

Science in the wider world

Staying warm in cold conditions and how we keep things warm introduces the concept of insulation, which can be linked to energy use in houses and how important insulation is in conserving energy.

Understanding that we all need food and drink is important when children look at the difficulties involved in growing food so that they can eat a healthy diet.

Review

The children could be assessed on their understanding of our basic needs as well as how much they know and understand about the similarities and differences between our needs when it is cold and our needs when it is hot.

Objectives
● To know what it is that makes us human and different from other living things.

Resources
A picture of a person; a picture of a dog; large and small sheets of paper

Speaking scientifically
mammal, similar, different, communicate

Lesson 2: What makes us human?

Introduction

Ask the children to look at the picture of the dog and the picture of the person and ask them to tell you what the similarities and differences are. They should be aware that both are mammals. Make sure that some of their observations relate to the senses: for example, dogs can smell better than we can. It might be interesting to compare how dogs and people communicate: we can talk but dogs only bark. Do the children think that dogs communicate with each other? How do they do this if they can't use words?

Whole-class work

1. Focus now on the picture of the dog and ask the children to describe what a dog looks like. Make sure they include fur, four legs and a tail. Write down the descriptions where they can be seen.

2. Ask the children to tell you what a dog can do. Make sure that this includes barking, wagging its tail and having a good sense of smell. Write down these characteristics where the children can see them.

Group work

3. Ask the children to work in groups of four and write two headings on their paper: 'What dogs can do that we can't' and 'What we can do that dogs can't'.

4. Discuss each group's answers with the whole class.

5. Write down the following questions and statements and ask each group to suggest answers. Some likely responses are provided after each question:

● Why can't a dog answer the telephone? (It has paws not hands; it barks and doesn't talk.)
● Can we communicate with a dog? (We give it instructions such as 'walk', 'sit', 'lie down' and so on, and it obeys. A further question might be: *Does a dog understand what we are saying to it?*)
● Why don't dogs have to wear clothes? (They have fur and we don't.)
● How does a dog tell us that it is happy? (It wags its tail, wriggles about and jumps up and down.)
● How do we tell each other that we are happy? (We use our faces to smile and our voices to laugh.)
● Why does a dog carry everything around in its mouth? (It doesn't have hands and so can't grip anything.)

> **Differentiation**
> ● Support children when they are trying to answer the questions and make sure that everyone takes place in the discussion.
> ● Challenge the children to explain how dogs communicate with each other.

Science in the wider world

All creatures have to communicate with each other. We still use words – either spoken or written – but computers and mobile phones have made it easier to communicate without seeing the other person. Facial expressions such as smiling and frowning are still important and tell the person we are communicating with how we are feeling.

Review

The children could be assessed in how well they can list what we can do, what a dog can do, and how we are different.

Objectives
● To recognise and understand some differences between mammals.

Resources
Photographs of different mammals displayed around the room; photocopiable page 41 'Mammals'; interactive activity 'Carnivore or herbivore?' on the CD-ROM; reference books about mammals; coloured pencils

Speaking scientifically
mammal, carnivore, herbivore

Lesson 3: Differences between mammals

Introduction
Ask the children to look at the animals on the photographs that are displayed on the walls. Make sure that there is a range of mammals from a mouse to an elephant as well as some that are carnivores and some that are herbivores. Include mammals from this country, especially cows and sheep, rabbits and foxes. As you point to each one ask, what it is called.

Whole-class work
1. Show the children a picture of a lion and ask them if they know what it eats. Explain that meat-eating animals are called carnivores.

2. Show them a picture of a cat and ask them if they think it is a carnivore. Ask them how they know and explain that cats live in towns and in the countryside and eat mice, rats and rabbits.

3. Show the class a picture of a zebra and ask them what they think it eats. Explain that grass- and plant-eating animals are called herbivores. (The terms 'omnivore' and 'insectivore' don't need to be used in this lesson unless some children already know them and introduce them into the discussion.)

4. Show the class a picture of a cow and ask them if they think it is a herbivore. Ask them how they know and discuss the importance of cows for milk, cream and cheese.

5. Discuss how carnivores and herbivores eat and explore different jaws and teeth by looking at some of the photographs of different mammals.

Group work
6. Give each child photocopiable page 41 'Mammals' and tell them that they can discuss their answers with other children at their table.

7. Show them the space underneath the picture of each mammal and explain to them that first of all they have to write the name of each mammal. Provide reference books if necessary.

8. The next thing they have to do is to write 'C' if the animal is a carnivore or 'H' if it is a herbivore. They could complete the interactive activity 'Carnivore or herbivore?' on the CD-ROM.

9. When they have finished labelling each mammal ask them to choose one carnivore and one herbivore to colour in, and then to complete the two sentences:
● The herbivore I have chosen eats _____.
● The carnivore I have chosen eats _____.

Differentiation
● Support children in naming the mammals and deciding which are carnivores and which are herbivores. Some children will need help with spelling and writing the names of the mammals on their photocopiable sheets.
● Challenge children to explain why some herbivores eat certain things, for example, giraffes and elephants can eat leaves that are high up in the trees. They might be able to explain why herbivores need to eat for many hours every day but carnivores such as lions spend a lot of time asleep.

Science in the wider world
This lesson begins to ask questions about what different mammals eat. Food chains, which are explored in Spring 2, are important because they help children to understand that if the chain is broken and certain foods become scarce, some animals will not have enough to eat and will die.

Review
The children can be assessed on the names of individual mammals and whether they can recognise which ones are carnivores and which ones are herbivores.

Objectives
● To understand what it means to be healthy.

Resources
Photocopiable page 42 'My healthy day'; coloured pencils

Speaking scientifically
hygiene, exercise, diet, medicines

Lesson 1: Staying healthy

Introduction

Discuss with the children what they think they need to do to stay healthy. Write down some of the key ideas, such as hygiene and keeping clean, exercise, eating the right food, medicines and having the right amount of sleep. It is important that the children begin to recognise and explore the links between exercise and keeping them fit; between eating the right foods and maintaining a healthy weight; and between medicines and prevention and cure of illnesses.

Whole-class work

1. During the lesson it is important to use the children's experiences rather than any secondary sources.

2. Ask them what they did before they came to school that will help them stay healthy. Some of the answers should include eating breakfast, walking to school, having a shower, washing their hands. Write some of the key words down where the children cans see them.

3. Talk to the children about what happens in school that keeps them healthy. They should know about PE and games lessons to keep them fit and a meal at lunchtime giving them energy to go through the rest of the day.

4. Ask them what they will do after school that will keep them healthy. Some of the answers might be: walking home, playing games, eating a meal, washing and showering, cleaning their teeth and going to sleep.

5. Ask them a series of questions such as: *Why is it important for your health that you eat regular meals? Why is exercise important? Why do you need to keep yourself clean?*

Individual work

6. Give each child photocopiable page 42 'My healthy day' and ask them to complete each of the three sections with as many healthy things as they do in one day.

7. They should also choose two of their ideas in each section and illustrate each one by drawing a coloured picture.

Differentiation
● Support children when they are completing their photocopiable sheet. Some children will need help with both ideas and spellings. If this is too difficult, it may be appropriate to accept illustrations only.
● Challenge children to write lists of types of healthy and unhealthy foods and to explore how exercise affects their hearts, blood flow and their lungs and breathing.

Science in the wider world

Understanding what it means to have a healthy lifestyle is important for their future health and beginning to explore the links between exercise and diet, for example, will help in this understanding. Exploring health in these broad terms will also help them in some of the themes in the next chapter.

Review

The children could be assessed on what they know and understand about their lifestyles and why diet, exercise and hygiene are important. They need to begin to ask questions about what healthy foods they eat and how much exercise they should be taking, but these are subjects that will be explored in detail in the next chapter.

Objectives
● To know what our senses are, how essential they are and how we use them.

Resources
An onion; crisps; sugar; ice; rulers; photocopiable page 43 'Senses'; interactive activity 'Senses' on the CD-ROM

Speaking scientifically
smelling, tasting, hearing, seeing, touching

Lesson 2: Senses

Introduction
Ask the class what they think their five senses are and write them down where everyone can see them: seeing, hearing, tasting, smelling and touching. Ask them to look around the classroom and tell you what they can see and make a list underneath 'Seeing'. Repeat for hearing and touching.

Whole-class work
1. Show the class the onion and ask them what it is. Ask them which sense they used to identify it as an onion. Cut the onion in half. Tell them to close their eyes and pass it round. Ask them what sense they could use this time to identify it (smelling).

2. Put some sugar in a dish and ask them what it is. You might get answers such as salt, sugar or even flour. Ask them which sense they used. Choose three volunteers and tell them to close their eyes. Ask them to put a few grains on their tongues and then tell you what it is. Ask them which sense they used this time (tasting).

3. Hold up a plate with some crisps on it. Ask them what they are and which sense they used to identify the crisps. Tell them to close their eyes and then either eat or crush some crisps. Ask them if they could hear what you were doing – they should say yes but identifying the noise with crisps is probably more difficult.

4. Show them some ice and ask them to describe what they see. One of the descriptions should be that the ice will be cold. Ask them to tell you how they know whether the ice is cold; ask two or three volunteers to touch the ice.

5. Ask: *Why is it important to know what something is before we eat it?* Discuss how our senses help us to identify whether something is safe to eat and emphasise how we need our senses in order to stay alive.

Individual work
6. Each child should complete photocopiable page 43 'Senses' or the interactive activity 'Senses' on the CD-ROM.

7. When they have finished look at the two questions and discuss their answers.

> **Differentiation**
> ● Some children will need help suggesting which senses they use when they are eating.
> ● Challenge children to answer more questions about which senses they use. For example: Which senses do they use most when they cross the road? Which senses might they use walking across their bedroom in the dark?

Science in the wider world
Obviously using their senses is an important part of interpreting the world they live in. One of the important links could be to understand the problems faced by people who have lost one of their senses, such as sight or hearing. Another issue could be safety, for example, crossing the road safely means seeing and hearing.

Review
Children could be assessed on whether they know all five senses and whether they can match their senses to an actual activity: for example, eating with tasting and smelling.

Objectives
● To understand the importance of senses to different animals.

Resources
Pictures of dogs and cats (including lions and tigers), herbivores such as deer or zebras and a chimpanzee; drawing paper; pencils and coloured pencils; felt-tipped pens; photopiable page 43 'Senses'; media resource 'What do these animals do?' on the CD-ROM

Speaking scientifically
seeing, hearing, tasting, touching, smelling

Lesson 3: Using our senses

Introduction

Use photocopiable page 43 'Senses', which the children will have already completed, and revise which part of their bodies they use to smell, hear, touch and so on.

Ask: *Which senses do you use when eating your food? Which senses do you use when you cross the road?*

Whole-class work

1. Use the media resource 'What do these animals do?' on the CD-ROM or show the children pictures of different animals and discuss what these animals do. For example, dogs and cats eat meat, they catch other animals, they run fast, and so on; zebras eat grass and run away from lions.

2. When they see the picture of the chimpanzee ask them what it can do that the other animals can't. The children need to understand that chimpanzees can hold things in their hands.

3. Discuss the lion, zebra and chimpanzee. Show them each of the pictures in turn and ask: *Why does it need to see well? Why does it need to hear well? Why does its sense of smell have to be very good? What would happen if it couldn't see or hear very well?*

4. It is difficult to understand taste when this sense is applied to animals but the children could discuss whether zebras need to taste when choosing grass to eat. Whiskers help cats feel the size of spaces they are moving through; chimpanzees must use their hands like ours and be able to feel the things they are holding.

Individual work

5. Ask the children to draw one of the animals they have been making observations about and to label the parts of its body it uses for its senses. Tell them that they must say what it uses each sense for. For example, if they are drawing a zebra and label its ears they should add something like – for listening for lions.

6. Some of these drawings could be used at the end of the lesson to remind the children of the different ways animals use their senses.

Differentiation
● Support children when they are labelling their drawings. Linking an animal's body part to its senses should be relatively easy but some children will find explaining why their chosen animal needs to use their senses in certain ways quite difficult.
● Challenge children to use secondary sources to find out more about how different creatures such as birds and reptiles use their senses.

Science in the wider world

It is important for children to explore a wide range of living creatures and to understand how they live and what their needs are.

Review

Children could be assessed on their understanding of how to match senses to parts of their bodies and to be able to do the same with other animals. They also need to understand why our senses are important, for example taste when we eat, sight for a lion when chasing its prey, and hearing for a zebra when something might be stalking it.

Objectives

- To assess whether the children can name parts of the human body.
- To assess whether the children can understand what different parts of the body are used for.
- To assess whether the children can recognise that human beings have different characteristics.

Resources

Photocopiable sheet 'Parts of the body' on the CD-ROM; rulers; adult volunteers

Working scientifically

- Using their observations and ideas to suggest answers to questions.

Understanding the human body

Revise

- Remind the children what they have been learning about in this chapter. Use one or two volunteers and point to various parts of their bodies: arm, ankle, foot, elbow, head, shoulders and so on. Ask what each part is called and write down the names where the children can see them.
- Use two different volunteers and ask the children to tell you which part of their bodies they would use to: pick something up, walk, speak, bend, sit down, kick a ball, throw a ball and lift something. Before they give you any answers ask the volunteers to mime each of the movements.
- Ask the children to look at their partners and to tell each other of any differences they can see such as eye colour, hair colour and so on.
- Ask the children what the five senses are and which part of their bodies they use for each one. Make sure that the sense and part of the body match: for example, taste and tongue; smell and nose.

Assess

- Each child should complete the photocopiable page 'Parts of the body' from the CD-ROM. They need to use their rulers to draw lines from each of the words to the appropriate part of the body and there are phrases or sentences that have to be completed by writing in the missing word in the space and then using their rulers and pencils to join the sentences to the correct part of the body.
- At the bottom of the photocopiable page the children should write down the answer to the question: *How am I different from my friend?* Their answer should include that they are taller or shorter, heavier or lighter, that their eyes and hair are the same or different colours and, if they remember, that their fingerprints and hand spans were different.

Further practice

- A more practical activity would help children to meet some of their objectives more easily. They could each make a head by sticking strips and small pieces of paper onto a balloon in several layers using PVA glue and then, after painting the head realistically with their hair and eye colour, either label the parts (eyes, ears, nose, forehead, cheeks and so on) directly onto the head, or hang labels from the suspended head using cotton.
- They could work in groups with adult help and use chicken wire and strips of paper and PVA glue or plaster-impregnated bandages to make a human body, which then needs to be painted realistically and labelled with as many parts of the body as possible.
- If a 3D whole body is too challenging, it is possible to use a similar method of construction to create a solid relief of a body mounted onto thick card.

Objectives
● To assess whether the children understand what it means to be alive.
● To assess whether the children understand the difference between things that are alive and things that are dead (no longer alive).
● To assess whether the children understand the difference between things that are dead (no longer alive) and things that have never been alive.

Resources
A wide range of pictures of animals, insects and birds, and household goods such as kettles, irons, spoons, knives; physical examples for the children to hold and touch including objects made of rubber and wood, rocks, sand, salt, metal objects and different plants and leaves together with dead plants and leaves; sticky notes; large display paper

Working scientifically
● Identifying and classifying.
● Using their observations and ideas to suggest answers to questions.

'Living', 'dead' and 'never been alive'

Revise

● Most of the revision will be asking children to classify the objects and pictures that are on display. It is important to keep the numbers of objects and pictures manageable. There should be no more than two of each of the following: mammals, insects, birds and plants; plus three dead objects and three that have never been alive.

● Ask the children how they know that they are alive. Their answers should include that they are able to breathe, eat, move, grow and have babies.

● Ask them how they know that a pet dog is alive. Their answers should be similar.

● Ask them how they know that a tree or one of the school's pot plants is alive. Their answers should include that they grow, feed and have flowers and seeds.

● Display as many of the pictures and objects as possible and number each of them. Ask the children to work with a partner. Give each pair a sheet with the numbers on. Ask them to look at each picture or object and write down after each number either 'D' if they think it is dead, 'A' if they think it is alive or 'NA' if they think that the object has never been alive.

● When they have finished, look at each object with the whole class and discuss whether their answers are correct. Useful questions to ask them include: *Why do you think it is alive? Why do you think it is dead? How do you know that it has never been alive?*

Assess

● Watching the children classifying the numbered objects and the subsequent discussion with the whole class will tell you whether they have understood the three categories of 'alive', 'dead' or 'never been alive'.

● A useful way to assess each individual is to give each child a sheet of paper and a pencil and ask them to work on their own to complete the following statements or follow the instructions. Tell them to use the pictures and objects to help them:
  ● Write down three things that are alive.
  ● Write down three things that are dead and not alive.
  ● Write down three things that have never been alive.
  ● I am alive because I _____.

Further practice

● A lot of the work that the children have completed can be used as a large display. One of the ways that will help reinforce their knowledge is to set a quiz for other children in different classes.

● Use a display board with a table underneath it. Mount a selection of numbered photographs on the display board and place a selection of numbered objects on the table.

● The children from different classes can be invited to complete a quiz by sticking a sticky note on the picture or objects 'D' for dead; 'A' for alive and 'NA' for never been alive.

● Children who have completed this chapter could take it in turns to be on hand to offer advice and to tell the children completing the quiz whether or not they have the correct answers.

Objectives
● To assess whether the children understand the difference between things that are dead (no longer alive) and things that have never been alive.

Resources
A selection of wooden objects such as spoons, wooden toys and wooden desks or tables; a selection of dried foods such as pasta, flour and a chocolate bar; a selection of metal and plastic objects; examples of their own toys (preferably those made from a range of materials); photocopiable page 'Toys and food' from the CD-ROM; rulers

Working scientifically
● Identifying and classifying.
● Using their observations and ideas to suggest answers to questions.

'Dead' and 'never been alive'

Revise
● This assessment activity follows on from Assess and review 2 and looks in more detail at the difficult distinctions between objects that are now dead but were once alive and objects that have never been alive.
● Show the children some of the objects that are dead but were once alive. For example if you show them a wooden spoon, ask them how they know that it isn't alive. They should suggest that it isn't moving or breathing and that it won't grow and you can't feed it. Ask them where wood comes from and lead them to the idea that the piece of wood that no longer breathes and grows was once part of a live tree that did grow and needed food to stay alive.
● Show the children some of the foods, such as pasta and flour. Once again, ask them how they know that the spaghetti is not alive. They should repeat some of their previous answers and suggest that it doesn't breathe, doesn't grow and so on. Ask them what they think spaghetti is made from. They may not know that it comes from wheat and will need to be told. It would be useful if you could show them an ear of corn and point out which parts are used to make flour. When they know that it is made from wheat, talk about grasses and how they know that grass is alive.
● Show the children plastic and metal objects and discuss how we know that these have never been alive. (But see the note regarding plastic on page 20.) Metal objects, for example, are made from a piece of rock/mineral which has never been alive.
● If necessary repeat these kinds of questions and discussions with other objects.

Assess
● Give each child photocopiable page 'Toys and food' from the CD-ROM. Briefly explain the three pictures: the train made from wood, plastic and metal, the sandwich and the bowl of pasta.
● Ask them to draw lines from each of the things – for example, the wooden part of the toy, or the spaghetti – and write 'D' for dead but was once alive or 'NA' for something that has never been alive.
● Talk through the answers with the whole class.

Further practice
● Many things that the children can see in the classroom, or have at home, or eat, are examples of things that are dead or have never been alive. Most of these things will have been made from original materials that may or may not have once been alive. Showing the children how some of these things are made from the original object, for example, a tree into a wooden chair, would reinforce some of the things that they have been learning about in this chapter.
● For example, show the children the actual process of making a wooden object: from cutting down the living tree, to the factory making a table or a chair. Similarly, show them the process of digging for iron ore and using furnaces to make the iron and steel and then manufacturing a metal spoon. Their clothes might also be useful examples that can be used for further practice: if they are wearing wool from sheep or cotton from a plant, they will be able to categorise these clothes as 'dead but once alive'. If any of their clothes are polyester, they are made from things that have never been alive.

The human face

- Label the face with as many parts as you can.
- Colour in the face to look like you.

I can label the parts of a face.

How did you do?

PHOTOCOPIABLE

■ SCHOLASTIC
www.scholastic.co.uk

Living and not living

■ Colour in the pictures of things that are living.

I can identify things that are living.

How did you do?

Feeding, growing, reproducing and breathing

■ Read the questions and put a tick or cross next to each picture.

Which of these feed?	Which of these grow?

Which of these reproduce?	Which of these breathe?

I can identify living things.

How did you do?

Animals and their young

■ Draw a line from each young animal to the adult that it will grow into.

■ Complete the sentences at the bottom of the page.

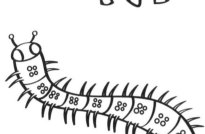

1. I am a mammal because I can _____.

2. I grow from a _____ into _____.

I can identify what young animals grow into.

How did you do?

Parts of a plant

■ Draw lines to match each label to the correct part of the plant.

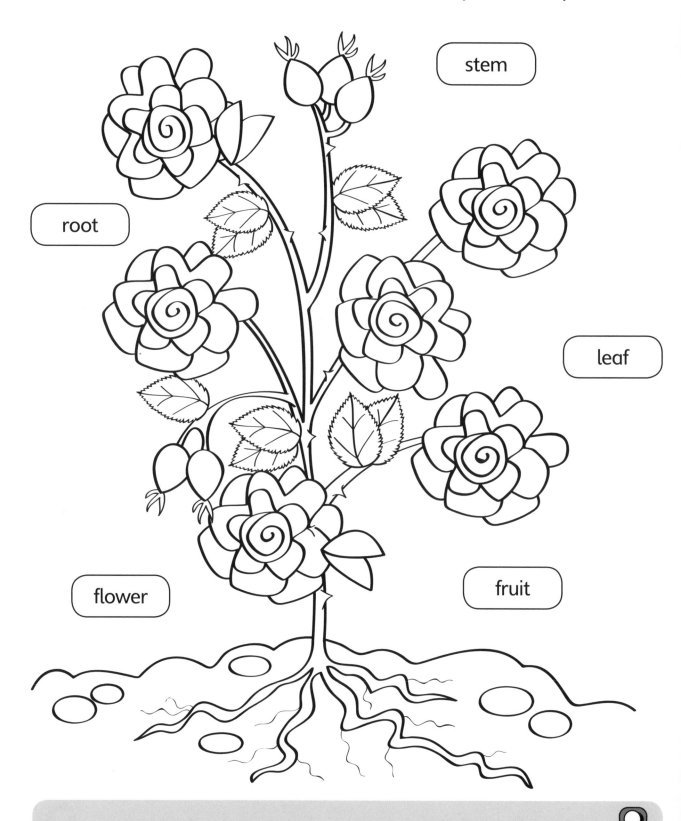

stem

root

leaf

flower

fruit

I can label the parts of a plant.

How did you do?

Mammals

■ Write the name of each mammal below its picture.

■ Next to each picture write 'C' for carnivore or 'H' for herbivore.

_____

_____

_____

_____

_____

_____

_____

_____

_____

I can identify mammals.

How did you do?

Name: _____

Date: _____

My healthy day

- Write down all the healthy things you do in one day in the table below.
- Draw pictures for two things from each column.

Before school	During school	After school

I can identify healthy activities.

How did you do?

PHOTOCOPIABLE

SCHOLASTIC
www.scholastic.co.uk

Name: _____   Date: _____

Senses

- Draw lines to match each sense with the correct part of the body.
- Answer the questions at the bottom of the page.

Hearing

Seeing

Tasting

Touching

Smelling

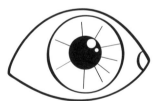

1. Which senses do you use when you are crossing the road?

_____

2. Which sense do you use most? _____

I can match senses to parts of the body.

How did you do?

Animals, including humans

Expected prior learning

● Know the names of living animals including mammals, birds, reptiles, amphibians, invertebrates and insects.
● Know the names of different plants including trees, flowers, vegetables and mosses.
● Understand how all living things grow.
● Understand how living things need to eat and move.

Overview of progression

After completing this chapter they should know about:

● the life cycles of humans and other creatures (insects and amphibians)
● human growth and growth in other animals
● the basic needs of babies and adults
● what we need to eat to stay healthy
● hygiene, keeping clean and caring for our teeth
● the importance of exercise.

Creative context

● This chapter provides opportunities for children to make observational drawings and to use different visual images to illustrate their findings. They will need to use charts, diagrams and drawings to produce attractive wall displays.
● Cooking pizzas or making healthy sandwiches will help the children to understand more about what healthy food is and its importance.

Background knowledge

Animals, including humans, have many similarities as well as differences. Animals and plants both reproduce but in different ways, and the children will already have some understanding that some animals grow in different ways.

Living creatures

There are different stages of human growth – from babies to grandparents. Other mammals also grow in specific stages, but carnivores and herbivores sometimes have different needs. Other animals, such as birds, frogs and butterflies, have very different patterns of growth.

Staying healthy

There are different kinds of food that will help us to stay healthy. Keeping clean is important, we need to look after our teeth and exercise appropriately.

Speaking scientifically

● You may wish children to look closely at some of the words associated with life cycles in frogs and butterflies, such as 'metamorphosis' and 'pupae'.
● In the lessons on healthy food it is important that children begin to understand the problems with fats and sugars and the need to eat more carbohydrates, fruit and vegetables.

Preparation

You will need to have available: pictures of a wide variety of animals and plants, including examples at different stages of their life cycles of frogs, butterflies and birds, pictures and real examples of different healthy and less-healthy foods or their packaging; simple restaurant menus; pictures of carnivores' and herbivores' teeth; a range of different papers of different sizes; rulers; glue; paints; stopwatches; adult volunteers; small mirrors; magnifying lenses; assorted feathers and, if possible, butterfly wings; chocolate biscuits; children's own toothbrushes and tootpaste; pictures of athletes; highlighter pens

On the CD-ROM you will find: photocopiable pages 'When we were born', 'The life cycle of a frog', 'The life cycle of a butterfly', 'The life cycle of a bird', 'Hygiene'; interactive activities 'Healthy eating', 'Life cycles', 'Healthy food'; media resources 'Spiders or insects', 'Human life cycle'

Chapter at a glance

Week	Lesson	Curriculum objectives	Objectives	Main activity	Working scientifically
1	1	• To revise the objectives of Year 1. • To identify and name a variety of common animals.	• To reinforce the idea that there is a range of common animals with both similarities and differences.	Identifying and naming a variety of animals that can be found in their homes and gardens.	• Observing closely. • Identifying and classifying.
	2	• To notice that animals, including humans, have offspring which grow into adults.	• To know the different stages in the human life cycle.	Discussing stages of growth – babies, children, parents, grandparents – and comparing and describing the different stages.	• Using their observations and ideas to suggest answers to questions.
	3	• To notice that animals, including humans, have offspring which grow into adults.	• To understand what 'growth' means using themselves as practical examples.	Discussing and comparing their own birth weights and the average size of new-born babies. Producing a class chart to show birth months.	• Gathering and recording data.
2	1	• To notice that animals, including humans, have offspring which grow into adults.	• To understand the growth cycle of mammals. • To recognise that the young of herbivores and carnivores have different characteristics.	Discussing the growth and needs of two mammals – a carnivore and herbivore.	• Using their observations and ideas to suggest answers to questions.
	2	• To notice that animals, including humans, have offspring which grow into adults.	• To understand the life cycle of a frog.	Discussing what amphibians are and finding out about a frog's life cycle. Labelling and recording facts on a diagram.	• Observing closely.
	3	• To notice that animals, including humans, have offspring which grow into adults.	• To understand the life cycle of a butterfly.	Discussing the life cycle of butterflies. Labelling and recording facts on a diagram.	• Observing closely.
3	1	• To notice that animals, including humans, have offspring which grow into adults.	• To understand the life cycle of a bird.	Discussing the life cycle of birds. Labelling and recording facts on a diagram.	• Observing closely.
	2	• To find out about and describe the basic needs of animals, including humans, for survival.	• To understand the different characteristics and needs of a variety of creatures.	Discussing differences between birds, frogs, insects, humans and other mammals.	• Use simple features to compare living things.
	3	• To find out about and describe the basic needs of animals, including humans, for survival.	• To recognise some similarities between different creatures and to understand their similar needs.	Discussing similarities between birds, frogs, insects, humans and other mammals.	• Use simple features to compare living things.

Chapter at a glance

Week	Lesson	Curriculum objectives	Objectives	Main activity	Working scientifically
4	1	• To find out about and describe the basic needs of animals, including humans, for survival.	• To begin to understand which foods are healthy and which are less healthy.	Creating lists of what is eaten over a day. Completing an interactive activity. Discussing what is healthy and what is less healthy referring to a food diary.	• Gathering and recording data to help in answering questions.
	2	• To find out about and describe the basic needs of animals, including humans, for survival. • To describe the importance for humans of exercise, eating the right amounts of different types of food, and hygiene.	• To understand that the food we eat can be broken down into food groups.	Discussing carbohydrates, proteins and fruit and vegetables and matching them to what they eat. Recording data on colour-coded pictures and in sentences.	• Using their observations and ideas to suggest answers to questions.
	3	• To find out about and describe the basic needs of animals, including humans, for survival. • To describe the importance for humans of exercise, eating the right amounts of different types of food, and hygiene.	• To understand what a healthy diet is.	Discussing foods that contain sugar and fat. Producing a healthy menu.	• Using their observations and ideas to suggest answers to questions.
5	1	• To describe the importance for humans of exercise, eating the right amounts of different types of food, and hygiene.	• To understand the importance of washing our hands.	Discussing why we need to wash our hands and learning how to do it properly. Completing an activity on washing hands before and after activities.	• Using their observations and ideas to suggest answers to questions.
	2	• To describe the importance for humans of exercise, eating the right amounts of different types of food, and hygiene.	• To understand the importance of caring for our teeth.	Discussing what our teeth are for and why teeth are important for all mammals. Investigating why it is important to clean and look after our teeth. Completing individual tooth diagrams.	• Gathering and recording data to help in answering questions.
	3	• To describe the importance for humans of exercise, eating the right amounts of different types of food, and hygiene.	• To understand the relationship between the food we eat and how healthy our teeth are.	Discussing high sugar foods using concrete examples such as sweets. Identifying sugary foods.	• Gathering and recording data to help in answering questions.
6	1	• To describe the importance for humans of exercise, eating the right amounts of different types of food, and hygiene.	• To know why exercise is important.	Discussing how we exercise and which parts of our body we use. Labelling arms, legs, heart and lungs on a diagram.	• Using their observations and ideas to suggest answers to questions.
	2	• To describe the importance for humans of exercise, eating the right amounts of different types of food, and hygiene.	• To understand their own daily exercise activities. • To learn how they can do more exercise.	Discussing what exercise they usually take each day. Making individual exercise diaries and small group discussions about improving the amount they take.	• Using their observations and ideas to suggest answers to questions.
	3	• To describe the importance for humans of exercise, eating the right amounts of different types of food, and hygiene.	• To begin to understand the effect exercise has on their pulse rate.	Discussing heart and pulse rates and measuring it at rest and after exercise.	• Gathering and recording data to help in answering questions.
Assess and review					

Objectives
- To reinforce the idea that there is a range of common animals with both similarities and differences.

Resources
Media resource 'Spiders or insects?' on the CD-ROM showing how many legs they have; photocopiable page 69 'Sharing a home'; coloured pencils

Speaking scientifically
similarities, differences, the names of a range of living creatures

Lesson 1: Identifying living things

Previous knowledge
The children should know the names of a range of animals including mammals, insects and reptiles. If they have completed Chapter 1 they should also be able to discuss similarities and differences and know what many animals need to stay alive.

Introduction
Begin by asking the children what animals they think live in their house and garden. Make a list of these and identify them as mammals, insects, amphibians, birds and so on. Their answers should include mammals, such as dogs, cats, hamsters and guinea pigs, but they may also have pets that are reptiles like snakes and lizards, or frogs and newts in their gardens. Introduce the idea that there are lots of other animals that live in the house and garden, such as flies, birds and spiders. They might even suggest foxes. Ask them which animals they like living near to them and which they don't. If they have birds in their garden, do they know their names? They should have all seen blackbirds, sparrows and probably robins. If you have time, it would be interesting to make a bar chart of the most popular pets.

Whole-class work
1. When you have a list of animals ask the children to classify them by asking: *Which ones are mammals? Which ones are insects? Which ones are birds?*

2. Give each child photocopiable page 69 'Sharing a home' and tell them that it shows a few of the animals that might live in anyone's house.

3. Ask them to identify what each creature is: for example, a fly is an insect; a blackbird is a bird.

4. Ask: *What are the similarities and differences between a fly and a blackbird?* They both use their wings to move through the air but are very different creatures. *What about the differences between a cat and a blackbird – or a cat and a rabbit?* This might be more difficult because they are both four-legged mammals, but one is a carnivore and the other is a herbivore. Consider what they look like, but also what they need. It is important to reinforce the idea that all creatures need food and shelter, and that all creatures need to breathe and to reproduce.

5. Ask the children what the similarities and differences are between a spider and a fly. Show them the media resource 'Spiders or insects?' on the CD-ROM and ask them to count the legs. Make sure that they understand that a spider is not an insect. They might know that a spider is a different species – it is an arachnid.

6. Ask the children whereabouts in the house and garden they would find the animals on the photocopiable sheet. They could draw lines from each animal to an appropriate place in the house or garden. It is important that they begin to understand that different creatures live in different habitats. For example, a bird needs to fly in the air but it also needs places to find food and build a nest; some insects need dark places; some creatures like to be dry and others like to be moist.

7. Discuss the various places where the children have put the different animals.

Individual work
8. Tell the children to colour in the pictures of the animals on the photocopiable sheet.

9. They should think of some more mammals, insects, birds and so on to add to the sheet, and draw them in an appropriate place.

Checkpoint
● Can you name a mammal/ bird/fish/reptile/amphibian/ invertebrate?
● How is a person different from a dog?
● How is a dog different from a butterfly?
● How do animals change as they get older?
● What can you do that you couldn't do when you were a baby?
● What can an adult do that a child can't?
● What do all animals need to stay alive?

Introducing the new area of study

It is important that all the children appreciate the huge range of different creatures and that although they do have similar needs – food, shelter and so on – they often live in different places.

Show pictures of a diverse range of animals, including humans; try to include some more unusual creatures such as a duckbilled platypus, or a rhinoceros beetle. Do the children know what they are called? Can they invent an appropriate name? Explain that they will be learning about all sorts of animals, including humans, and that although they may look very different, they all have similar needs.

Differentiation
● Support children who might have difficulty drawing lines to put the animals in appropriate places.
● Challenge children to find out more about some of the animals in the house and garden. Why might they live in these places? They could have a look around their house and garden to see what different creatures they can find and identify. Are the animals in their home similar to those on their sheet – and similar to those a friend has in his or her home?

Science in the wider world

Thinking about local environments such as their house, garden and school grounds and what lives there will be important in later chapters and when the children are exploring habitats.

Review

The children could be assessed on their knowledge of what different creatures need to remain alive and their understanding of the similarities and differences between the creatures that live in their houses and gardens.

Objectives
● To know the different stages in the human life cycle.

Resources
Pictures of babies, children, young people, adults and old people; photocopiable page 70 'Me as a baby'; media resource 'Human life cycle' on the CD-ROM; pencils; paper

Speaking scientifically
growth, babies, toddlers, adults

Lesson 2: The human life cycle

Introduction

Before this lesson and lesson 3, give each child photocopiable page 70 'Me as a baby' to take home, together with an accompanying letter. The letter should explain why you need the information on the photocopiable sheet, and that the class will be looking at the human life cycle and human growth as part of the science curriculum. A sensitive approach will be needed, especially if some children have been adopted: they and their adoptive parents may not know the answers to the questions on the photocopiable sheet. If you feel that this will be an issue it would be better not to use the children's own information but to find another way to explore this part of the curriculum.

Whole-class work

1. Show the children some of the pictures that are displayed around the room. Ask them whether they are babies, toddlers, children, adults or old people. Ask: *How do you know?*

2. It is important that the children begin to understand that human beings grow and change. They don't stay the same.

3. Using the media resource 'Human life cycle' on the CD-ROM, show a picture of a baby and a toddler side by side and ask the children to tell you what they think the differences are. Repeat this with toddler and child, child and adult, and adult and older person.

4. Another important question is: *What can an adult do that a toddler can't?*

Group work

5. Give the children sheets of paper and tell them that they can talk about what they are going to write but that each person has to write their own answers to the questions. Ask them to write down each of the questions or statements and their answers:

- Write down five things you can do now that you couldn't do when you were a baby.
- Write down three differences between you and an adult.
- What can you do that a toddler can't?
- What can you do that a grandparent can't?

6. Before finishing the lesson remind the children to complete the photocopiable sheets at home and to return them to school together with a photograph of themselves as babies.

> **Differentiation**
> ● Support children with their writing. Some of them may be able to tell you all kinds of appropriate answers but could find the writing and spelling difficult.
> ● Challenge children to consider how they think they have grown and developed in school. Ask them what they can do now that they couldn't do when they started school.

Science in the wider world

The idea of growth, change and development is an important concept when applied to humans and other creatures. For example, mammal growth from birth to old age is very different from the metamorphosis that takes place in tadpoles and butterflies.

Review

The children could be assessed on their understanding of how humans progress through various stages of their growth, both in their written work and group discussion.

Objectives
● To understand what 'growth' means using themselves as practical examples.

Resources
A photograph of each child; photocopiable page 70 'Me as a baby' (completed and returned from home); photocopiable page 'When we were born' from the CD-ROM; paper; crayons; glue

Speaking scientifically
growing, learning, moving, talking, thinking, taller, heavier, bar chart

Lesson 3: Human growth

Introduction

Ask the children what they think 'to grow' means. Their answers might include plants growing from seeds, puppies growing into dogs, and trees growing from acorns. Ask: *How have you grown since you were a baby?* The children should tell you that they are taller and heavier. Ask: *What can you do that babies can't?* The children's responses should include talking and walking. Discuss the completed photocopiable sheets 'Me as a baby' to establish when children learn to do these things.

Whole-class work

1. The class needs to be organised so that the children can do most of the work during the group activities.

2. The aim of the group work is to produce bar charts using the data provided on the completed photocopiable pages 'Me as a baby' from the CD-ROM and to mount these photocopiable sheets with their baby pictures attached.

3. Tell the children that they will use their photocopiable sheets and their photographs to make an exhibition called 'Who am I?'.

4. Tell the children that they are going to create a bar chart showing the months in which they were born.

5. Use the whiteboard and write down names of the children alongside the month of their birth

6. Remind the children how to create a bar chart.

Group work

7. Ask the children to make a bar chart on their photocopiable page 'When we were born' from the CD-ROM. Remind them to colour in the columns of blocks so that they are easy to see.

8. Allow them to mount their photographs and completed photocopiable sheets 'Me as baby' as a display.

9. Allow other children to see whether they can recognise who each baby is from their photographs.

10. When the bar charts are finished, make sure that the children know which are the most common and least common birth months.

> **Differentiation**
> ● Support children when they are producing the bar chart. They will need to count the number of children in each month as well as colour in the blocks for each month accurately.
> ● Challenge the children to use the information they have to make their own bar chart, for example: When did we walk? The horizontal axis should be divided appropriately from 6 to 24 months.

Science in the wider world

Interpreting data and being able to display it in more accessible ways such as charts and graphs will be useful in all other subjects.

Review

The children can be assessed on their understanding of the ways they have changed and grown since they were babies. They also need to be able to explain that although the changes from being a baby to being a child in Year 2 are similar, they don't always happen at the same time. For example, their completed photocopiable sheets, 'Me as a baby', will show differences in when they learned to talk and walk.

Objectives
• To understand the growth cycle of mammals.
• To recognise that the young of herbivores and carnivores have different characteristics.

Resources
Photocopiable page 71 'Mammals and their young'; pictures and/or DVDs of a variety of mammals and their young (including lions and antelopes, zebras or gazelles); rulers

Speaking scientifically
carnivore, herbivore, mammal, growth, growing

Lesson 1: Growth in mammals

Introduction
Write down the following question: What are the differences between each mammal and its young? Allow the children five minutes to walk around the room with a partner and look at all the pictures of mammals and their young. If possible, show them wildlife DVDs of mammals with their young. Make sure that they include carnivores and herbivores.

Discuss the differences that the children have identified. Some of the answers should include: differences in size; the young animals can't live on their own or move properly; some young mammals depend on their parents for food.

Whole-class work
1. Ask the children what they know about carnivores and what they know about herbivores. Make sure that they understand the basic difference between meat eaters and plant eaters.

2. Point to the different pictures of mammals and ask: *Which are carnivores and which are herbivores?*

3. The children need to see examples of new-born herbivores and understand that they are usually able to see, move and even run straight away. There are many wildlife programmes that show this happening in countries such as Africa. Sheep and lambs in this country are another good example.

4. Ask the children why these animals need to be able to see and move straight after they are born. Discuss the fact that herbivores are hunted by carnivores and have to be able to get away from them.

5. Show the children examples of the babies of carnivorous animals, such as lion cubs and kittens. Ask: *How are these babies different from those of herbivores?* They should suggest that they can't see or move properly and are often without hair or fur.

Group work
6. Ask the children to complete photocopiable page 71 'Mammals and their young' by drawing a line from each adult to its baby.

7. Ask them to colour in the mammals that they think are carnivorous.

Differentiation
• Support children who might find it difficult to identify the differences between carnivorous and herbivorous mammals and match adult mammals to their offspring.
• Challenge children to write down why they think carnivorous babies, such as lion cubs, can be born blind and helpless and still survive and grow up.

Science in the wider world
Understanding the differences between carnivorous and herbivorous mammals, together with how one can't survive without the other, will help with exploring food chains and recognising how many plants and animals are dependent on each other.

Review
Children could be assessed on how good they are at identifying the names of mammals and how well they understand the differences between how those that eat meat and those that don't grow from baby to adult.

Objectives
• To understand the life cycle of a frog.

Resources
Pictures of frogs; photocopiable page 'The life cycle of a frog' from the CD-ROM; A4 paper; coloured pencils; glue; scissors; interactive activity 'Life cycles' on the CD-ROM (This lesson will work much better if the children have access to a pond during early spring and can actually see frogspawn, tadpoles and froglets.)

Speaking scientifically
amphibian, tadpole, frogspawn, froglet

Lesson 2: Frogs

Introduction
Use the pictures around the room to explore some of the differences between frogs and mammals. It is also important to explain some of the similarities, such as: breathing air; needing food and shelter; growing and moving. Tell the children that a frog is an amphibian and explain briefly what this is: a cold-blooded animal that lives partly in water and partly on land.

Whole-class work
1. Discuss briefly with the children the similarities between them as new-born babies and them as they are now. Emphasise the idea that what they have in common is such things as two legs, two arms, fingers and toes and that they will always need to breathe air. Make sure they understand that this will carry on throughout their lives as they continue to grow up and grow older.

2. Use pictures and DVDs to explain the frog's life cycle from an adult frog laying eggs (frogspawn) in water to tadpoles without legs, and tadpoles with legs living in water, through to froglets and adult frogs, who are able to live on land and in water. This will be much easier if you can show the children how this happens in an outdoor pond.

3. Ask the children what the frog's needs are at various stages in its life cycle. There will be differences between stages (a tadpole needs water to live and breathe oxygen through but a frog doesn't) and similarities (both need food and oxygen).

4. The children could create some closely observed drawings at each of the stages.

Individual work
5. Each child needs photocopiable page 'The life cycle of a frog' from the CD-ROM and a separate piece of A4 paper. They will also need coloured pencils, scissors and glue or you can use the interactive activity 'Life cycles' on the CD-ROM.

6. Use the photocopiable sheet to quickly show them a frog's life cycle and ask them to colour each section.

7. They should then cut out each box and stick it onto their blank piece of paper in the correct chronological order.

8. Ask them to label each section with the words 'frog', 'frogspawn' and 'tadpole'.

Differentiation
• Support children who need help with reading the names during the frog's life cycle. Some children may also need help with remembering the order of development.
• Challenge children to find out how tadpoles breathe in water and how the way they breathe changes as they grow their legs and grow into froglets that spend most of their time on land.

Science in the wider world
At different stages of their development frogs have different needs. How habitats meet various creatures' needs is explored in a later chapter; this is in an important area of science because it leads to the exploration of the importance of conservation.

Review
The children can be assessed on their understanding of the sequence of events and changes in a frog's life cycle. They should also now understand some of the similarities and differences between the growth and life cycle of a mammal and that of a common amphibian.

Objectives
● To understand the life cycle of a butterfly.

Resources
Pictures of butterflies, caterpillars and pupae; photocopiable page 'The life cycle of a butterfly' from the CD-ROM; interactive activity 'Life cycles' on the CD-ROM; A4 paper; coloured pencils; glue; scissors

Speaking scientifically
eggs, caterpillar, pupa, metamorphosis

Lesson 3: Butterflies

Introduction

Briefly discuss with the children the life cycle of a frog and remind them of what their needs are at each stage and how they are sometimes different. Remind them how the tadpole grows and changes into a froglet (they lose their tail and gain their legs), and remind them how different this is from their changes from baby to child to adult (they always have the same number of legs and arms; they just get bigger).

Whole-class work

1. Use the pictures around the room to discuss the life cycle of a butterfly. Make sure the children understand that the adult butterfly lays eggs, that a caterpillar hatches from the eggs and then feeds on leaves before turning into a pupa, and that eventually a butterfly emerges from the pupa case and starts the whole process again.

2. Discuss with the children the differences between how a butterfly and caterpillar feed: the butterfly uses flowers for nectar, which is sweet, and the caterpillar eats green leaves. Emphasise how dependent the butterfly's life cycle is on plants as food.

3. Look at the differences in appearance between a butterfly and a caterpillar. Remind the children that a butterfly is an insect. Ask: *How many legs does an insect have?* Use pictures of butterflies to illustrate symmetry: this can be extended into art with large paintings of symmetrical butterflies.

Individual work

4. Give each child photocopiable page 'The life cycle of a butterfly' from the CD-ROM and a separate piece of A4 paper. They will need coloured pencils, scissors and glue. (Or you can use the revelant screen from the interactive activity 'Life cycles' on the CD-ROM.)

5. Discuss the different sections on the photocopiable sheet and briefly remind them of the butterfly's life cycle. The pictures show the life cycle of a peacock butterfly.

6. Ask the children to colour in each picture and then cut out each box and stick them onto the separate piece of paper.

7. Ask them to label each section with the words 'butterfly', 'eggs', 'caterpillar' and 'pupa'.

> **Differentiation**
> ● Some of the words are difficult and children will need support in spelling and writing them. Support children who need help with organising the boxes from the photocopiable sheet in the correct order.
> ● Challenge children to find out how long each stage of the life cycle lasts.

Science in the wider world

Butterflies and caterpillars are dependent on flowers and plants. This means that if we are going to have butterflies in the future then the conservation of plants is important.

Review

The children could be assessed on their understanding of the butterfly's life cycle and their ability to place each of the stages in the correct order.

Objectives
● To understand the life cycle of a bird.

Resources
Pictures of different kinds of common British birds, their nests, eggs and fledglings (if possible, use DVDs to show birds hatching from eggs and fledglings being fed); photocopiable sheet 'The life cycle of a bird' from the CD-ROM; interactive activity 'Life cycles' on the CD-ROM; sheets of A4 paper; coloured pencils; glue; scissors

Speaking scientifically
feathers, beaks, nests, eggs, fledglings

Lesson 1: Birds

Introduction
Look at the pictures around the room and ask the children if they know the names of some of the common birds that they are likely to see in their gardens and around the school. Talk about their different colours and the range of foods that they eat.

Whole-class work
1. Discuss the life cycle of birds with the children, making sure that you explain that birds build nests before laying their eggs and that the eggs have to be kept warm before they hatch. The children need to be aware that baby birds are blind, featherless and helpless but do have beaks, wings and legs that grow and develop as the baby birds become older.

2. Ask the children what they had to learn to do when they were still babies. One of their answers will be that they learned to walk. Ask them what they think baby birds have to learn to do.

Individual work
3. Give each child photocopiable page 'The life cycle of a bird' from the CD-ROM and a separate sheet of plain A4 paper. They will also need scissors, coloured pencils and glue. (Or you can use the relevant screen from the interactive activity 'Life cycles' on the CD-ROM.)

4. Tell the children to colour in the picture in each of the four separate boxes.

5. Next, ask them to carefully cut out each box and glue each of them onto the blank A4 sheet in the correct order of the bird's life cycle.

6. They could label the pictures: 'Adults build a nest'; 'Adult lays eggs'; 'Baby birds hatch'; 'Fledglings are fed by their parents'.

Differentiation
● Support children who might need help understanding the correct sequence of events when they are sorting and gluing their four pictures of the bird's life cycle. Some children may also need help cutting out the four boxes accurately.
● Challenge children to use secondary sources to find out more about some common British birds. For example: *What do they eat? How are their nests different? What colour are their eggs?*

Science in the wider world
During this chapter, and in later ones, the children will learn more about bird habitats and what they need to eat to stay alive. This will lead directly to exploring habitats and how we need to make sure that we conserve the ones we have now and find ways to create more.

Review
The children could be assessed on whether they understand the bird's life cycle and the progression from egg to adult bird. They could also be assessed on their understanding of how baby birds are fed and what they need to learn to do before they can live as an adult bird.

Objectives
• To understand the different characteristics and needs of a variety of creatures.

Resources
Pictures of mammals, birds, amphibians (frogs) and butterflies; close-up pictures/ DVDs of butterflies and birds showing legs, beaks, feathers, butterfly wings and a butterfly head and tongue; paper; pencils; magnifying lenses; assorted feathers and, if possible, butterfly wings

Speaking scientifically
the names of the animals in the pictures, difference

Lesson 2: The differences between animals

Introduction

Show the children pictures of various mammals and ask them to tell you the differences between each animal and a human. For example: most mammals have four legs but we have two; they can't talk; they have fur all over them; their heads are different from ours. Show them a picture of a frog and a dog. Ask them what the differences between these are. They should tell you that a frog lives partly in water and a dog doesn't; it is cold blooded, has clammy skin and absolutely no hair; it also lays eggs but a dog doesn't; and its babies (tadpoles) grow in a very different way.

Whole-class work

1. Show the children a picture of a British butterfly that they might see in the school grounds, such as a peacock or a tortoiseshell. If possible, use close-ups of wings, legs and heads. Ask them to describe what it looks like. If available, use DVDs that show butterflies flying and eating. They should notice that a butterfly has a long tongue for reaching nectar, wings with dusty scales, six legs and multi-faceted eyes.

2. Ask them to quickly describe a butterfly's life cycle, making sure they understand the different stages from egg through caterpillar to pupa.

3. Show the children a picture of a common garden bird that they are likely to see around the school or at home. A robin would be a good example. Ask them to describe it. They should notice its beak, two quite scaly legs and its feathers.

4. Ask them to describe a bird's life cycle, making sure that they understand the changes from egg to newly hatched baby bird to fledgling.

5. Ask them to tell you some of the differences between birds and butterflies. Make sure that the children are aware of the following differences: the different number of legs; feathers versus wing scales; beaks versus long tongues; birds look after their eggs but butterflies don't; birds don't go through a pupa stage; birds look after their babies and feed them but butterflies don't.

Individual work

6. If it has been possible to find butterfly wings and feathers, use the magnifying lenses and ask the children to look closely and to draw what they can see. (Check first that none of the children are allergic to feathers.)

7. Ask the children to use their paper and pencils to write a list of differences between birds and butterflies. They could illustrate some of their answers.

> **Differentiation**
> • Support children by helping them to understand and write down some of the differences. Those children who are finding it difficult could be asked to find only two differences.
> • Challenge children to find out about what happens inside a bird's egg as the chick inside it grows and develops, ready for hatching.

Science in the wider world

Understanding differences between living things is important in science. Children also need to be able to closely observe all kinds of materials and make accurate scientific drawings.

Review

The children could be assessed on their understanding of at least five differences between butterflies and birds.

Objectives
• To recognise some similarities between different creatures and to understand their similar needs.

Resources
Use the same pictures of mammals (including an ape), birds, amphibians (frogs) and butterflies that were used for the previous lesson together with the same close-up pictures

Speaking scientifically
the names of the different creatures in the pictures and their body parts, similar

Lesson 3: Similarities between animals

Introduction
Show the children some of the pictures of various mammals. Talk about how they think they are the same as – or similar to – humans. Encourage the children to look carefully at the pictures but to think beyond what they can actually see. For example, they should understand that mammals and humans all have eyes, ears and noses and that apes, like humans, often use two legs for standing. They are also similar in that mammals, including humans, have live babies and they all need to breathe, eat and shelter from heat or cold.

Whole-class work
1. Use the range of photographs and ask the class some or all of the following questions:
   • *What similarities can you see between this bird and this butterfly?* (Use common British examples, such as a robin and a peacock butterfly.) Make sure the children's answers include: they both have heads and eyes and have to eat; they both fly; they both lay eggs; they both breathe.
   • *What similarities can you see between the bird and the frog?* Make sure that their answers include: they both lay eggs; they both breathe; they both eat and have mouths that can be seen; they both have two eyes.
   • *What similarities can you see between a human and insects and a frog?* Make sure answers include: they all have eyes and mouths; they all need to eat and see.
During the discussion try to make the distinction between how different creatures look the same and their similar needs.

Group work
2. Ask the children to complete the following statements by writing down four answers for each one. The first statement is about what they can see when they look at the pictures and what they know about each creature, and the second statement is about common needs:
   • The creatures are similar because they all have:
   • All of the creatures have these similar needs:

> **Differentiation**
> • Support the children in understanding what the basic needs of all living creatures are. Some children will need help when writing down their answers during the group work.
> • Challenge the children to look at the different needs: for example, all creatures need to eat. Ask them to find how frogs eat, how butterflies eat, how we eat and so on.

Science in the wider world
All creatures have basic needs that must be met if they are going to survive. As the children grow older they will need to explore how we can make sure all creatures can eat and have the right habitats to move, grow and reproduce.

Review
The children could be assessed on how many similarities they can find between a wide range of different creatures. They should also be able to tell you the common basic needs of eating, breathing, reproducing and moving.

Objectives
● To begin to understand which foods are healthy and which are less healthy.

Resources
Photocopiable page 72 'My food diary' (The children need to know in advance that they will be completing this food diary. The day before the lesson tell them either to think carefully about what they eat during the day or to write down some of the things they have eaten); interactive activity 'Healthy eating' on the CD-ROM; pictures of healthy foods (such as salads, fruits, vegetables, pasta and a balanced meal)

Speaking scientifically
the names of all kinds of food

Lesson 1: What we eat

Introduction
Ask the children questions about what some of the animals from previous lessons eat. For example: *What does a dog eat? What does a cow eat?* Use some animals that they know less well, such as a frog, zebra, elephant, robin and so on. It is important that the children know that there is a wide range of things that are eaten and that they include meat, fish and plants.

Whole-class work
1. The children should have come prepared with lists and ideas of what they have eaten the day before, or they could use what they have already eaten today as examples.

2. When discussing what the children have eaten, it is important to write down a list of the foods they suggest. This could be on an easily seen whiteboard or a list could be typed out, quickly photocopied and given to each group of children.

3. Ask the children for some examples of breakfasts they have eaten. If they say cereals, explain to them that these will include cereal, milk and probably also sugar.

4. If their lunch has been sandwiches at school, ask them to imagine taking the sandwich apart. It will include such things as bread, butter, cheese, tomatoes, ham, lettuce and so on.

5. When they tell you about the snacks they have eaten, remind them that crisps are potatoes and that chocolate bars will include sugar.

6. Talk briefly about which foods they think are really healthy and which they think might not be very healthy. Complete the interactive activity 'Healthy eating' on the CD-ROM.

Group work
7. Give each child photocopiable page 72 'My food diary' and ask them to complete it.

8. Tell them to talk about their diaries with other children on their table and to ask other children to help them decide what to write when they complete the two statements at the bottom of the photocopiable sheet.

> ### Differentiation
> ● There are lots of food names that the children will not be familiar with so it is important to support them when they are completing their food diaries. If some children find writing very difficult, it will be important for an adult to help them to write down their suggestions.
> ● Challenge children to include drinks in their diaries and to break down their lunch and evening meal choices into as much detail as possible.

Science in the wider world
Diet and nutrition are very important. Children need to know which foods are unhealthy and which foods they should eat more of. Eventually, foods and what they eat can be related to weight, health and fitness.

Review
Children could be assessed on their responses to the statements at the bottom of the photocopiable sheets. What they write might give you some indication as to what they already know about healthy eating.

Lesson 2: Food groups

Introduction
Ask the children to look at their completed food diaries from the previous lesson and to spend a short time talking to the person sitting next to them about the foods they ate that were healthy and the ones that they think might have been unhealthy. Tell them to find as many as they can.

Whole-class work
1. Show them pictures and examples of various carbohydrates, such as cereals, rice, pasta and bread. Ask them to name each one. Tell them that these are carbohydrates, which will give them energy to run and walk.

2. Show them pictures or examples of cheese, meat, beans and eggs. Ask them what each one is and tell them that these foods are proteins, which will help them to grow.

3. Show them pictures and examples of fruit and vegetables and ask them what each one is called. Tell them that fruit and vegetables help to keep them healthy.

4. Explore the idea that these types of foods are combined to make meals: spaghetti bolognaise, pizza and fruit pies should be familiar to the children. Discuss the ingredients in each one. For example: spaghetti bolognaise is pasta (carbohydrate), meat (protein) and tomatoes (fruit); pizza is wheat-flour dough (carbohydrate), tomatoes (fruit), cheese (protein) and possibly ham (protein).

Group work
5. Give each child photocopiable page 73 'Healthy food' or use the interactive activity 'Healthy food' on the CD-ROM.

6. Show the children the food types and make sure they know their names.

7. Ask them to complete the photocopiable sheet on their own, but when they are making their choices of which foods to colour, allow them to talk to other children on their table about the kinds of foods that they think are healthy.

Differentiation
● Support children who have difficulty recognising various foods and make sure that they understand which foods are healthy. Some children will need support when they are writing their answers on the photocopiable sheet.
● Challenge children to break down other meals into different food groups. They could try fish and chips, roast dinner or beans on toast.

Science in the wider world
Nutrition is important and understanding what it means to eat a healthy diet is an essential life skill. Classifying food that the children are likely to eat as 'healthy' and 'less healthy' might begin to challenge some of the problems related to overeating.

Review
Children could be assessed on their understanding of which food falls into which group, as well as their ability to recognise the kinds of food that keep them healthy.

Objectives
• To understand what a healthy diet is.

Resources
Photocopiable page 74 'Less-healthy food'; photographs or real examples of foods (butter, margarine, chocolate, cheese, carrots and apples); coloured pencils; examples of simple restaurant menus (for the layout not necessarily the content)

Speaking scientifically
protein, carbohydrate, fruit, vegetable, fat, sugar

Lesson 3: Creating a healthy menu

Introduction
Remind the children of the different types of food that they explored when they completed photocopiable page 73 'Healthy food'. Look carefully at some of the names of the foods with them again and ask them whether they have eaten any fruit or vegetables already today. If they have, ask them what they were. Ask them if they will be eating any for lunch or their evening meal. Ask them what food they like best and try to link as many of their choices as possible with the three categories on the photocopiable sheet.

Whole-class work
1. Discuss with the children why they think we should only eat small amounts of fats (such as butter and margarine) and sugary foods. Raise the issue that too much fat (crisps, cakes and biscuits) might make us put on too much weight, and too much sugar (chocolate and fizzy drinks) can cause problems with our teeth. Be aware that weight can be an extremely sensitive subject and it is important that children who may be overweight are not made to feel that there is something wrong with them or looked down on in any way.

2. Discuss with the children the kinds of foods that they should eat lots of, such as fruits, vegetables, pasta, bread, rice, peas, tomatoes, apples and so on.

3. Many children do not always eat as many fruits and vegetables as they should. Remind them about being able to eat fruit and vegetables in different ways. For example, pizzas and spaghetti bolognaise (pasta and tomatoes) and apple crumbles (without too much sugar).

4. If possible, parents could come into school and cook dishes using lots of vegetables and fruits (veggie burgers and salads, for example). Local restaurants may have chefs who are willing to show the children how to cook fruit and vegetables in ways that are both tasty and nutritious.

Group work
5. Ask the children to complete photocopiable page 74 'Less-healthy food'.

6. Show the children what a three-course menu looks like and ask them to work with a partner to write a menu of their own, with only one dish per course in each section. The title is 'A healthy menu'. Their finished menus can be part of a larger display on healthy eating.

Differentiation
• Support children who might find understanding some of the concepts difficult, especially when they are writing out their healthy menu.
• Challenge children to think of more than one dish per course for their healthy menu.

Science in the wider world
Children need to make healthy choices about what they eat. Identifying foods that they can eat lots of and foods that they shouldn't will help them to make appropriate choices and live healthier lifestyles.

Review
Children could be assessed on how healthy their menu actually is. For example, how many examples of fruit, vegetables and carbohydrates are there in each of their dishes?

Objectives
● To understand the importance of washing hands.

Resources
Photocopiable page 'Hygiene' from the CD-ROM; coloured pencils; scissors

Speaking scientifically
hygiene, germs, illness

Lesson 1: Hygiene

Introduction
Ask for several volunteers to tell you (or demonstrate) how they wash and dry their hands. Make sure they mention soap, hot water, rinsing the soap off their hands and drying them with clean towels or with paper towels. Ask them why they think public toilets mainly have hot-air dryers.

Whole-class work
1. Explain to the class why they need to wash their hands. Discuss germs that cause food poisoning and colds. There is no need to go into any greater detail about germs and bacteria or other illnesses.

2. Use a practical example of someone with a cold sneezing and then blowing their nose and touching a door handle. The next person to touch the door handle gets the cold germ on their hands and then eats a sandwich. If they haven't washed their hands they could transfer the other person's cold germs into their own mouths.

3. Explain that to avoid the cold this person washed their hands *before* they ate their sandwich – but sometimes we should wash our hands *after* we have done an activity: going to the toilet is an obvious example.

4. Finally, talk to the children about drying their hands. Use a practical example: someone with a cold doesn't wash their hands very well and dries them on a towel. The next person uses the same towel to dry their hands and could pick up the cold germ.

5. Ask the children the same question that you asked in the introduction: *Why do most public toilets have hot-air dryers?* The answer is that they are much more hygienic in a place used by lots of people. See whether the children can explain why they are more hygienic.

Individual/paired work
6. Give each child photocopiable page 'Hygiene' from the CD-ROM. Look at each box and explain quickly what is happening.

7. Ask them to colour each picture to make it look more interesting and then to cut each one out.

8. They have to arrange the pictures into two piles: 'Washing before I do this' and 'Washing after I do this'.

9. When they have arranged their piles they should talk to a partner about their decisions before the whole class discusses which of the activities each pile should contain.

Differentiation
● Support those children who find it difficult to complete their photocopiable sheet. Some children will find cutting out the boxes difficult and may need adult help.
● Challenge children to think about their school day and identify specific times when they will need to wash their hands.

Science in the wider world
Hygiene and its place in reducing illness and disease are obviously important. The children should be aware of how important this is in hospitals and where there is contact with babies and very old people.

Review
Children should be assessed on their understanding of when their hands need to be washed.

Objectives
● To understand the importance of caring for our teeth.

Resources
A picture of a carnivore's and a herbivore's teeth; photocopiable page 75 'My teeth'; small mirrors; coloured pencils; chocolate biscuits; children's own toothbrushes and toothpaste

Speaking scientifically
teeth, lower jaw, upper jaw, carnivore, herbivore

Lesson 2: Dental hygiene

Introduction
Show the children pictures of herbivores' and carnivores' teeth and ask them what differences they can see. Explain that a carnivore has sharp tearing teeth for biting and that herbivores have flatter teeth for grinding up vegetation.

Whole-class work
1. This lesson involves children looking at their own teeth, helping other children to look at theirs and eating a chocolate biscuit. A letter should be sent to parents and carers telling them that this will happen. Encourage parents to send in toothbrushes and toothpaste for the children to use after they have eaten a chocolate biscuit.

2. Ask the children to feel their teeth and to tell you what shapes they think their teeth are. Explain to them the difference between the shape of their front biting teeth and the back flatter teeth that can grind and chew.

3. Ask them what they have eaten already today and what they might eat during the rest of the day.

4. Ask them to explain which teeth they need for certain kinds of food. An apple is a good example because it needs biting (front teeth) and then chewing (back teeth).

Paired work
5. Explain to the children that they will be looking at their teeth and helping their friends to look at theirs. Explain that they will also be eating a chocolate biscuit and looking again at their teeth. Tell them that those who have brought in their toothbrushes will be able to clean their teeth at the end of the lesson.

6. Give out photocopiable page 75 'My teeth', the mirrors and coloured pencils. Explain to the children how to look at their teeth with the mirror and how to help other children to look at theirs.

7. Tell them to complete the diagram.

8. Explain that they will eat the chocolate biscuit and then look at their teeth again.

9. Ask: *Why should we clean our teeth after meals?* Listen to some of their answers with the whole class and supervise the children cleaning their teeth.

> ### Differentiation
> ● Support children who struggle with looking at their teeth and then marking the correct ones on their sheet.
> ● Challenge the children to find out some of the names of different teeth.

Science in the wider world
There are many health issues associated with teeth and it is very important to keep them clean. Children need to learn about how to clean them, how plaque develops, what kinds of food to avoid and that dental treatment including fillings will help maintain healthy teeth as well as good health.

Review
Assess the children on how much they know about the differences between herbivores' and carnivores' teeth and the depth of their answers when they are asked: *Why should we clean our teeth after meals?*

Objectives
● To understand the relationship between the food we eat and how healthy our teeth are.

Resources
Photocopiable page 73 'Healthy food'; coloured pencils; pictures of a selection of foods or examples of actual food (chocolates, biscuits, sweets, cakes, apples, pears, carrots, fizzy drinks, pasta, tinned tomatoes, pizza)

Speaking scientifically
teeth, lower jaw, upper jaw, plaque

Lesson 3: Dental hygiene and diet

Introduction
Talk to the children about what they saw when they used a mirror to look at their teeth after they had eaten a chocolate biscuit. Make sure that they know that pieces of biscuit and chocolate stuck in the spaces between their teeth would have stayed there until they used their toothbrushes to clean them.

Whole-class work
1. Ask the children what they think a chocolate biscuit is made of. Explain to them that the biscuit is made mainly of flour, butter and sugar and that the chocolate on top of the biscuit is made of cocoa and sugar.

2. Explain that too much sugar can be very bad for teeth, especially if sugar from a chocolate biscuit, for example, is left on their teeth without cleaning them properly.

3. Show the children a range of foods, including fizzy drinks, and ask them to tell you which ones they think have lots of sugar in them.

4. Make a list of the foods with large amounts of sugar that aren't very good for their teeth.

5. At the same time as they are identifying foods with sugar in them ask them to identify foods that are good for their teeth. Make sure that they include hard fruits and vegetables, such as apples and carrots (which clean your teeth as you chew them and massage your gums), and foods rich in protein and calcium (which strengthen teeth).

6. Tell them that whether they eat lots of foods with sugar in them or not they should clean their teeth at least twice a day.

Group work
7. Give each child photocopiable page 73 'Healthy food'. This should be a new copy, rather than the one that they completed in a previous lesson.

8. Ask them to colour in three foods that have lots of sugar in them and three foods that are actually good for their teeth.

9. Tell them to explain their choices to a partner.

> **Differentiation**
> ● Support children who might have difficulty recognising foods with lots of sugar.
> ● Challenge children to look at food labels on fizzy drinks, chocolate bars and biscuits. Can they find out which foods contain the most sugar?

Science in the wider world
The link between what we eat and our health is very important. Children need to know as much as possible about these links so that they can make appropriate healthy choices. As they grow older they will be able to understand more about the science of tooth decay.

Review
Assess the children on whether they can identify a range of foods that contain a lot of sugar as well as those that help keep their teeth healthy.

Objectives
- To know why exercise is important.

Resources
Sheets of paper; pencils; rulers; coloured pencils; pictures of athletes displayed around the room; access to the playground

Speaking scientifically
parts of the body, especially: arms, legs, heart, mouth, lungs

Lesson 1: Exercise

Introduction
Ask the children: *What do you think the word 'exercise' means? Can you give me some examples?* Make sure that their answers include: walking, running, skipping and jumping. Ask: *Why do you think exercise is important?* They should suggest that it helps us to keep healthy, stay fit and maintain the right weight. Some children may know that exercise also helps to keep our hearts healthy.

Whole-class work
1. Tell the children to look at the pictures of athletes that are displayed around the classroom and ask them to think carefully about which parts of their bodies they are using. Allow them to discuss their ideas with a partner.

2. Ask: *Which parts of your body do you use when you run?* Write the names of the parts down where all where the children can see them. Include legs, ankles, feet, knees, arms, lungs and heart.

3. Take them out to run round the playground and ask them if there are any parts of their bodies that they think they have missed out. Running uses many parts of the body, including leg muscles and ankle joints, and using them keeps them healthy.

4. Ask the children whether they were breathing more heavily and whether they could feel their hearts were beating faster. Explain that exercise makes them use their hearts and lungs more and keeps them healthy.

Group work
5. Tell the children to draw an outline of a human body – draw a simple one for them to copy or draw one and photocopy it.

6. They should write down all the parts of their bodies that they use when they run – legs, arms, knees, ankles, heart, lungs and so on – around the outline of the body.

7. Tell them to draw a line from each word to where it is on the body.

8. Show them how to draw the heart and lungs and ask them to draw these on their outline of the human body.

> ### Differentiation
> - Support children who need help when they are arranging and writing all the words around their outline of the human body.
> - Challenge children to find out what their hearts and lungs actually do.

Science in the wider world
It will be important to know how the heart and lungs work and that it is important to eat healthily and exercise regularly. Heart problems in later life as well as issues with weight can be linked to a poor diet and lack of exercise.

Review
The children can be assessed on the accuracy of how they label their outline of the human body.

Objectives
● To understand their own daily exercise activities.
● To learn how they can do more exercise.

Resources
Pictures of athletes from the previous lesson, photocopiable page 76 'Exercise diary', pencils, paper, highlighter pens

Speaking scientifically
running, jumping, skipping and so on, heart, lungs

Lesson 2: Daily exercise

Introduction

Remind the children of the different types of exercise that they talked about during the previous lesson. Use the photographs of different athletes to help them to remember running, jumping, sprinting and so on.

Whole-class work

1. Talk to the children about the fact that their bodies are designed to be active. Remind them of the different parts of their bodies that they used when they were running round the playground. Refer to the body outline that they completed during the last lesson.

2. Explain that all humans have to use their muscles to keep them strong. Ask the children to flex their arms to feel the muscle. Ask them to feel a partner's calf muscle. Explain to them that their heart is a muscle and that exercise is a good way to keep it strong and active.

3. Ask them about any exercise they do. This could include walking to school, PE lessons, activities out of school, playground games and so on.

4. Show them how to make an exercise diary – or provide photocopiable page 76 'Exercise diary'.

5. Tell them that they will be completing their own diary. To help them, ask for some suggestions for the 'At school' and 'At home' columns for the first day.

Paired work

6. Allow the children to complete their exercise diaries.

7. When they have finished, ask them to highlight the exercise they do regularly and to talk to a partner about their favourite exercise.

8. Tell the children to compare their diary with that of their partner. Ask: *Do you think you do enough exercise? How could you increase the amount of exercise you do?*

9. Ask them to complete this sentence at the bottom of the exercise diary: My favourite sort of exercise is _____.

> **Differentiation**
> ● Children who have difficulty writing will find completing the exercise diary difficult. A teaching assistant could help them by writing down their ideas for them.
> ● Challenge children to find out the kinds of training athletes have to do to be successful.

Science in the wider world

All children need to become aware of the difference between being active and being inactive. The importance of activity has to be a lifelong commitment that will help them to avoid heart problems and play a large part in preventing obesity. Being aware of the heart as a muscle that pumps blood around the body is also important and will be part of many future science lessons.

Review

Children can be assessed on their understanding of where their muscles are and which ones are used during exercise. They should also know a range of exercise activities and be able to suggest which ones are their favourites.

Objectives
● To begin to understand the effect exercise has on their pulse rate.

Resources
The exercise diary from the previous lesson; stopwatches; lots of adults or Year 6 children who can take pulses, count and operate a stopwatch; access to the playground

Speaking scientifically
heart, muscle, pulse rate

Lesson 3: Exercise and pulse rate

Introduction

Talk to the children about their favourite exercises. Ask them which muscles they use for some of the exercises. Make sure that as well as muscles in their legs and arms they understand that the heart is a muscle.

Whole-class work

1. This lesson involves either other children or adults checking and timing pulses on children's wrists. Send a short letter to each child's parents or carers telling them that this will happen as part of the science curriculum.

2. Take the children outside to run across the playground and ask them to feel their hearts beating faster. Ask them why they think that this happens.

3. When they are back in the classroom tell them that the heart is a muscle and works hard when they are running. Tell them that during exercise leg muscles, for example, need more blood and that the heart pumps this blood into the muscles.

4. Tell them how important it is to keep their hearts healthy and that exercise helps them to do this.

5. Explain to them how they can measure part of how their heart pumps by measuring their pulse rate. Show them how to do this. (This can be difficult. Use the wrist and fingers, not thumbs, because there is a separate pulse in the thumb. This is where adults and older children will be needed – to measure the pulse and work out how many 'pumps' a minute their heart is beating.)

6. Ask them to write two headings on their paper: 'Resting' and 'After exercise'.

Group work

7. Measure each child's pulse for a minute when they are resting and write it down. (Adults can do this by measuring the pulse for 15 seconds and then multiplying the number by four. This will give the pulse rate for a minute.)

8. After the children have run across the playground measure their pulse again and write it down.

9. Ask the children to look at the two numbers and they will see that their pulse rate is much higher after exercise.

10. Ask them why they think their pulse rate is higher. Explain that during exercise their heart is pumping their blood around their bodies faster.

11. Ask them to write down and complete this sentence:

● My pulse rate is higher after exercise because_____.

Differentiation
● This is a difficult lesson and children will need support in understanding their pulse rates and in completing the sentence.
● Challenge some children to look at the differences between pulse rates. Who has the biggest difference and who has the smallest? With some adult help they might be able to suggest why.

Science in the wider world

Some heart problems can be avoided by exercise and an appropriate diet. This is a lifelong commitment and needs to be part of the children's lifestyle choices.

Review

Children can be assessed on their understanding of what the heart does and their understanding of the effect exercise has on their pulse rate.

Objectives
• To assess whether the children understand that there are both similarities and differences between living things.
• To assess whether they know that different creatures have different life cycles.
• To assess whether they understand that living creatures have similar basic needs.

Resources
Pictures of babies and toddlers, pictures of babies and adults of various creatures including herbivores and carnivores; photocopiable pages 'The life cycle of a frog' and 'The life cycle of a butterfly' from the CD-ROM; writing paper; drawing paper; pencils; coloured pencils

Working scientifically
• Identifying and classifying.
• Using their observations and ideas to suggest answers to questions.

Humans and other animals

Revise
• Show the children pictures of human babies and toddlers and ask them to tell you what similarities and differences they can see. Discuss size, weight, how babies can and can't move and how toddlers can talk and babies can't. Repeat this with pictures of babies and adults of other mammals. Make sure that they understand that both babies and adult mammals, including humans, have ears, eyes, noses, legs and arms but that they develop the use of these features at different stages.
• Show them a picture of a lion or similar mammal and ask what they eat. Remind them that meat-eating animals are called carnivores. Show them a picture of a zebra or a cow and ask what they think it eats and remind them that mammals that eat grass and vegetation are called herbivores.
• Ask them to look at the shapes of different carnivores and herbivores. They will see similarities such as four legs, two eyes, fur, noses and ears and so on.
• Discuss some of the differences between carnivores and herbivores – herbivores have flatter teeth for grinding, and some herbivores have longer legs to run quickly and bigger ears to hear better.
• Another main difference between carnivores and herbivores is that carnivore babies are born blind and helpless and herbivore babies are able to walk and run almost immediately after they are born. Ask the children why this happens.
• Remind the children of some of the similar basic needs of all creatures (revised briefly in lesson 1). For example, they all need food, air and space to live in and all living creatures have to eat, breathe, move and reproduce.
• Show the children the life cycle of a butterfly and a frog from the photocopiable pages 'The life cycle of a butterfly' and 'The life cycle of a frog' from the CD-ROM and discuss how they grow in a very different way from mammals and humans. But, remind them that amphibians and insects still need to eat, breathe, move and reproduce – just as we do.

Assess
• Make sure that the children have paper for writing and drawing and both pencils and coloured pencils. Ask the children to complete the following sentences or answer the following questions:
  • What three things can you do now that you couldn't do when you were a baby?
  • Write down two things that your mother had to do for you when you were a baby that she doesn't have to do for you now.
  • Write down three differences between a carnivorous animal and one that is herbivorous.
  • What do the following creatures eat: lion, cow, frog, butterfly, zebra?
  • All living creatures have to: reproduce, _____, _____ and _____.
  • Draw the life cycle of a frog and label the drawing with these names: 'frogspawn', 'tadpole' and 'froglet'.

Further practice
• There is a lot of quite difficult material in this lesson but further practice could look at, drawing and labelling the life cycles of birds and/or butterflies.

Objectives

- To assess whether the children understand that what we eat should be healthy.
- To assess whether they can place common foods that they eat into three basic food groups.
- To assess whether they understand what kinds of food make up a healthy meal.

Resources

Pictures of different foods, or real examples of food; photocopiable pages 73 and 74 'Healthy food' and 'Less-healthy food'

Working scientifically

- Identifying and classifying.
- Using their observations and ideas to suggest answers to questions.

What we eat

Revise

- Ask the children to quickly write down what they have eaten so far today. If it is in the morning, tell them to include what they will be eating for lunch.
- Talk to the children about different food groups that will help them to stay healthy. For example: proteins will help them to grow strong bones and muscles; fruit and vegetables will keep them healthy and might stop some minor illnesses such as colds, throat infections and so on; carbohydrates will give them energy to run around at playtime. Write down three headings: 'Proteins', 'Carbohydrates' and 'Fruit and vegetables'.
- Talk to the children about different food groups that are less healthy, such as fats and sugar. Remind them that it would be better for their health if they ate less fatty food and less food with lots of sugar in it. Write down two more headings: 'Fats' and 'Sugar'.
- Look at some of the pictures of food – or the real examples – and ask them which column each should go in. In other words, are they proteins, carbohydrates, fruit and vegetables, fats or sugar?
- Use their examples of what they have eaten or will be eating today and write some of them in the five columns. Tell them that it is important to eat a balanced diet.
- Remind the children that foods such as cakes, pizzas and spaghetti bolognaise are made out of several different ingredients and that foods such as fizzy drinks, biscuits, crisps and chocolate bars contain fats and lots of sugar.
- It is important to relate food to health. They need to know why certain foods are not very healthy. This could be a very sensitive area with some children but it is important to link diet with weight, fitness and tooth decay.
- If you think that it is necessary, use photocopiable pages 73 and 74: 'Healthy food' and 'Less-healthy food'. Ask the children to work with a partner for a few minutes to look at the pictures and identify the types of food.

Assess

- Ask the children to complete these statements or answer these questions:
  - Write down three foods that are proteins.
  - Write down three foods that are carbohydrates.
  - Write down three foods that are fruit or vegetables.
  - Write down three foods that contain lots of sugar.
  - Write down three foods that contain lots of fats.
  - Write and draw a balanced one-course meal. It can be a proper sit-down meal, sandwiches or a picnic. You must label the different foods in your meal.

Further practice

- This is a difficult assessment and the children will have to write down the names of several different foods.
- For further practice ask them to create their own favourite pizza. They should write the names of the ingredients and label them 'P' for protein, 'C' for carbohydrate, 'FV' for fruit and vegetables, 'F' for fats and 'S' for sugar.

Objectives
● To assess whether the children understand the relationship between what we eat and healthy teeth.
● To assess whether the children know when they need to wash their hands.
● To assess whether they understand why exercise is important.

Resources
Pictures or a range of real examples of different foods (use the same examples from Assess and review 2); pictures or real examples of high-sugar foods; a picture of an athlete running;

Working scientifically
● Identifying and classifying.
● Using their observations and ideas to suggest answers to questions.

Hygiene and exercise

Revise

● Show the children pictures of different kinds of food (the same ones you used for Assess and review 2). Ask them which ones they think are good for their teeth and which are less good.
● Discuss briefly with the children foods that have a lot of sugar in them, such as chocolates and fizzy drinks. Ask them what they saw when they ate a biscuit and then looked at each other's teeth. Remind them that pieces of biscuit and chocolate had got stuck in the spaces between their teeth. Talk about the importance of cleaning their teeth at least twice a day. Tell them that this is important even if they don't eat many biscuits because lots of different foods can also stick in their teeth.
● Remind the children that eating fruits such as apples, or vegetables such as carrots, will help to keep their teeth clean and healthy.
● Talk to the children about why it is important to wash their hands. Make sure that they understand that it can prevent the spread of germs that can cause disease and make them ill. Ask them to tell you when they have washed their hands today. Make sure they include after going to the toilet and before eating their lunch.
● Ask them to tell you what kind of exercise they have done so far this week. Try to include running, skipping, jumping, walking to school, swimming, activities in PE and so on.
● Show the children the picture of an athlete running. Ask them which parts of the athlete's body are being used the most. Make sure they include legs, arms, ankles, knees, heart and lungs.
● Remind the children that the heart is a muscle and has to be exercised so that it stays healthy. Ask them how they have made their heart work hard this week. Their answers should reflect the kind of exercise they have done.
● When they measured their pulse rate in lesson 3, week 6, it should have shown them that their heart pumps harder after they have run around the playground. Remind them that this is because it is pumping the blood to their muscles and when they are running their muscles need more blood.

Assess

● Tell the children to:
    ● Write down three foods that aren't very good for your teeth.
    ● Write down three foods that will help to keep your teeth healthy.
    ● Washing your hands is important. Sometimes you should wash them before doing something and sometimes you should wash them after you have done something. Read each statement and write down 'B' for before or 'A' for after:
    Eating lunch
    Going to the toilet
    Cleaning out a hamster
    Playing with a dog
    Feeding a baby
    Making a sandwich
    ● Explain why it is important to do exercise.
    ● Write down three activities that will make your pulse rate higher.

Further practice

● There are all kinds of hygiene issues related to colds and sneezes and communicable diseases that children might be interested in.
● The heart is much more complicated than just being a simple pump and the children might want to look at diagrams of the heart and learn more about how it works.

Sharing a home

■ Draw lines to match each animal to somewhere it might live in the house or garden.

■ What else might live there? Draw pictures in the correct places.

I can match animals to their habitats.

PHOTOCOPIABLE

Me as a baby

■ Find out as much as you can about yourself as a baby.

■ Draw a picture of yourself in the space below.

1. Where were you born? _____

2. How much did you weigh? _____

3. How long were you? _____

4. What colour was your hair? _____

5. What colour were your eyes? _____

6. What made you laugh? _____

7. How old were you when you said your first word?

_____

8. How old were you when you learned to walk?

_____

I can show how babies change and grow into children.

How did you do?

PHOTOCOPIABLE

Mammals and their young

■ Draw lines to match each adult with its baby.

I can match adult mammals with their young.

How did you do?

PHOTOCOPIABLE

My food diary

■ Think about what you have eaten in a full day.
■ Complete the chart below.

Breakfast	Mid-morning snack
Lunch	**Afternoon snack**
Evening meal	**Anything else eaten**

1. The healthiest food I have eaten is _____.

2. The unhealthiest food I have eaten is _____.

I can identify the foods I have eaten.

How did you do?

PHOTOCOPIABLE   **■SCHOLASTIC**
www.scholastic.co.uk

Name: _____   Date: _____

Healthy food

■ Look at the pictures below and answer the questions.

Proteins	Carbohydrates	Fruit and vegetables

■ Complete these sentences:

1. Proteins help us to _____.

2. Carbohydrates give us _____.

3. Fruit and vegetables keep us _____.

4. Which foods in the pictures have you eaten today? _____

_____.

5. Colour in the foods below that you think are healthy.

I can identify different types of food.

How did you do?

Less-healthy food

■ Sort the different types of food into the correct boxes.

We should eat a small amount of these foods:	We should eat a medium amount of these foods:

butter   cheese   cream   chocolate   sausages
sweets   lemonade   biscuits   jam   cream cakes

I can identify some less heathly foods.

How did you do?

My teeth

- Look in a mirror at your teeth.
- On the diagrams below, lightly shade any teeth you have in grey.
- If a tooth is missing, leave it white.
- If a tooth has a filling, colour it black.

- Now eat a chocolate biscuit and look in the mirror.
- Colour the places where the biscuit has stuck, in brown.

I can identify which teeth I have.

How did you do?

Exercise diary

■ Complete the chart below to show how much exercise you do each day.

Day	Exercise done at home	Exercise done at school

■ My favourite sort of exercise is _____.

I can do identify different types of exercise.

How did you do?

Plants

Expected prior learning
- Can identify basic parts of plants.
- Can identify basic parts of flowers.
- Understand there are lots of different kinds of plant, some we use for food.
- Understand that flowers reproduce.
- Understand plants, like humans, need certain conditions in order to live.

Overview of progression
After completing this chapter they should know about the:
- main parts of a plant and its flower
- characteristics of what a plant needs to grow and survive
- pollination of flowers
- range of plants in the local environment
- kinds of plants that are used for food
- differences between seeds and how they grow
- ways plants protect themselves.

Creative context
- This chapter provides opportunities for children to make observational drawings and to design and create environments in which plants can grow.

Background knowledge
- There is an enormous variety of plant life, ranging from mosses and small flowers to huge trees.
- Plants, like animals, have needs: they need to reproduce. They need water, light and an appropriate temperature. They grow from a wide variety of different seeds. The seed does not look like the adult plant.
- Plants are at the beginning of every food chain, so are vital to life on earth, as well as absorbing carbon dioxide from the atmosphere.

Speaking scientifically
- Children will need to know the names of the basic parts of plants as well as the names of parts of flowers, as well as key words such as 'pollination', 'seeds', 'grow' 'food', 'habitat', 'local environment', 'temperature' and 'humidity' and the broad names for some plants, such as 'flowers', 'grasses', 'herbs', 'trees' and 'bushes'.

Preparation
You will need to provide: black paper; coloured pencils; string; thick wax crayons; marker pens; small sticky notes; paper plates; plastic cups and dishes; clear containers; red and blue food colouring; aprons; jam jars; trays; cotton wool; a large cardboard box; access to a fridge; seeds including cress, acorns, sunflower and broad beans; pictures of other seeds; real plants including dandelions and clover; photos of dandelions, clover, nettle leaves, magnified nettle leaves, holly leaves, a cactus, twigs of oak, pine, holly and hawthorn; photos or real examples of a variety of leaves; real flowers including a general bouquet, tulips or daffodils, white carnations; pollen-rich flowers, such as catkins; pineapples, large potatoes and onions; pictures of real examples of various fruits and vegetables including broccoli, carrots/parsnips, sweetcorn/rice/wheat, tomato/apple, celery, lettuce/cabbage; pictures of real examples of pizza or spaghetti bolognaise; photos or DVDs of parrots, sparrows, various herbivores; baby photos of humans and a variety of animals; a large bag of bird seed; a plank of wood with four or five lids firmly fixed to it to act as a bird table; a large picture of a meal containing meat, potatoes, carrots, peas and an apple pie; pots, trowels and compost; magnifying lenses and simple microscopes.

On the CD-ROM you will find: photocopiable page 'How plants drink'; media resources 'Parts of a plant (1)', 'Parts of a flower (1)', 'Parts of a flower (2)', 'Parts of a plant (2)'; interactive activities 'What do seeds grow into?', 'Animal or plant?', 'Food from plants', 'What plants need'

Chapter at a glance

Week	Lesson	Curriculum objectives	Objectives	Main activity	Working scientifically
1	1	• To revise the objectives of Year 1. • To identify and describe the basic structure of a variety of common flowering plants.	• To revise the names of parts of plants, including 'flower', 'stem' and 'roots'. • To begin to understand how plants grow and change.	Discussing the parts of plants from pictures and practical examples in the classroom and in the school grounds. Individual drawing and labelling the parts of a dandelion and creating a flower jigsaw.	• Identifying and classifying. • Observing closely.
	2	• To be introduced to the process of reproduction in plants.	• To know what the parts of flowers look like.	Discussing the parts of a flower and groups labelling a diagram. Taking apart a daffodil and drawing and labelling the parts.	• Observing closely, using simple equipment.
	3	• To be introduced to the requirements of plants for growth and survival.	• To know some differences and similarities between plants and animals.	Discussing animal and plant growth and needs in terms of food, warmth, shelter etc. Completing true/false sentences.	• Observing closely, using simple equipment. • Using their observations and ideas to suggest answers to questions.
2	1	• To be introduced to the process of reproduction in plants.	• To understand the importance of pollination.	Discussing the process of pollination. Using microscopes and lenses to observe and draw pollen. Completing a worksheet.	• Using their observations and ideas to suggest answers to questions.
	2	• To be introduced to the process of reproduction in plants.	• To understand the process of pollination and the life cycle of a common plant.	Discussing the role insects and the wind play in pollination and seed dispersal. Creating a 'hanging life cycle' of a dandelion.	• Using their observations and ideas to suggest answers to questions.
	3	• To use the local environment throughout the year to observe how plants grow.	• To begin to understand the wide variety of plants that grow in a small area. • To know that the same kind of plant can have leaves that are different.	Walking around the school grounds to identify different plants. Looking closely and drawing clover leaf patterns to compare.	• Observing closely, using simple equipment.
3	1	• To observe how plants grow.	• To begin to understand that plants are important sources of food. • To be able to identify which parts of different plants we eat.	Discussing what plants they eat, using practical examples. Creating an illustrated plate of plants they like to eat.	• Using their observations and ideas to suggest answers to questions.
	2	• To understand that seeds and bulbs have a store of food inside them.	• To learn that birds eat different types of seed. • To understand that birds help to disperse seeds.	Discussing the plants that mammals, birds, insects and reptiles eat. Using the school environment to survey seeds eaten by birds. Discussing seed dispersal.	• Gathering and recording data.
	3	• To find out and describe how plants need water, light and a suitable temperature to grow and stay healthy.	• To be able to identify the requirements for plant growth.	Discussing the needs of plants – warmth, light, food and water. Drawing pictures to show what plants need.	• Using their observations and ideas to suggest answers to questions.

■SCHOLASTIC

Chapter at a glance

Week	Lesson	Curriculum objectives	Objectives	Main activity	Working scientifically
4	1	• To find out and describe how plants need water, light and a suitable temperature to grow and stay healthy.	• To understand that plants need water to grow.	Discussing how to plant cress seeds and why they need water. Growing cress seeds with and without water.	• Performing simple tests. • Gathering and recording data.
	2	• To find out and describe how plants need water, light and a suitable temperature to grow and stay healthy.	• To understand that plants need warmth to grow.	Growing seeds in warm and cold conditions.	• Performing simple tests. • Gathering and recording data.
	3	• To find out and describe how plants need water, light and a suitable temperature to stay healthy.	• To understand that seeds do not need light to grow but plants do.	Discussing whether plants will germinate and grow best in light or dark conditions. Growing seeds in light and dark conditions.	• Performing simple tests. • Gathering and recording data.
5	1	• To observe and describe how seeds and bulbs grow into mature plants.	• To identify some differences between seeds.	Examining a range of seeds. Individual drawings of different seeds. Group planting of different seeds.	• Observing closely.
	2	• To observe and describe how seeds and bulbs grow into mature plants.	• To learn how potatoes, pineapples and onions begin to grow.	Discussing that most plants start from seeds but that there are other ways that plants grow. Recording growth using potatoes, pineapple tops and onions.	• Gathering and recording data.
	3	• To find out and describe how plants need water, light and a suitable temperature to grow and stay healthy.	• To learn how plants 'drink'.	Discussing what plants need to grow – light, warmth water, food. Group experiment on plants taking in water.	• Performing simple tests. • Gathering and recording data.
6	1	• To use the local environment throughout the year to observe how plants grow.	• To know some differences between deciduous and evergreen bushes and trees.	Discussing what 'evergreen' and 'deciduous' mean. Examining examples of leaves. Individual drawings and sentences.	• Using their observations to suggest answers to questions.
	2	• To use the local environment throughout the year to observe how plants grow.	• To know that there is a variety of leaf shapes in plants.	Sorting and classifying a variety of leaves according to chosen criteria. Individual drawings and leaf rubbings.	• Using their observations to suggest answers to questions. • Identifying and classifying.
	3	• To be introduced to the requirements of plants for survival.	• To understand the different ways that plants protect themselves.	Discussing why plants have to protect themselves and looking at examples of protection, such as spines, thorns and poison. Individual drawings of nettles and rose thorns.	• Using their observations to suggest answers to questions. • Gathering and recording data.
Assess and review					

Objectives
● To revise the names of the parts of plants, including 'flower', 'stem' and 'roots'.
● To begin to understand how plants grow and change.

Resources
Media resource 'Parts of a plant' on the CD-ROM; photocopiable page 102 'Plant jigsaw'; a bouquet of mixed flowers; a large image of a plant; plants in the classroom and school grounds; several dandelions dug from the ground with all their parts intact (if possible, try to obtain some still in flower, and some with the seeds); two pieces of medium-thickness A4 card per child; coloured pencils; scissors; glue

Speaking scientifically
root, stem, seeds, leaf, flower, above ground, below ground

Lesson 1: The structure of plants

Previous knowledge

The children should know some of the parts of a plant and be aware of some differences and similarities between humans and plants.

This lesson is reviewing previous knowledge about the structure of plants and making sure that every child understands the names of the parts of plants. The next lesson builds on this knowledge and looks more closely at the specific parts of a flower.

Introduction

Ask for a volunteer to stand at the front next to a large pot plant and ask them to describe what they see. They should identify such things as: it is green, lives in a pot, has a flower on it, grows in the soil, needs watering and so on.

Show the whole class the bouquet of mixed flowers. Ask them to describe some of the flowers. Take some of the individual flowers out of the vase so that they can see them more easily. Look at the different colours. Write down the range of colours. Try to identify some of the different shapes, the number of petals and so on.

Whole-class work

1. Show the children the media resource 'Parts of a plant' on the CD-ROM. Use volunteers to come to the front of the class. Ask: *Who can come and point to where the roots are? Who can point to the flower? Who knows which part is the stem?* All these words need to be written down where the children can see them.

2. Take the class into the school grounds to look at plants. Ask them to show you leaves – remind them that grasses, bushes and trees have leaves as well as obvious flowering plants.

3. Ask the children to show you examples of flowers, seeds and stems. Ask them what a tree trunk is. They should recognise it as a stem. Ask: *Why can't you see any roots?* They should know that roots grow underground – although it might be possible to see some tree roots on the surface.

Group work

4. Give each table a dandelion, complete with the parts that are found above and below the ground. Ask them to look carefully and find out where each part of the plant is. Ask them to complete these five sentences:

- A dandelion root looks like _____.
- A dandelion stem looks like _____.
- A dandelion flower looks like _____.
- A dandelion seed looks like _____.
- A dandelion leaf looks like _____.

Individual work

5. Give each child a sheet of art paper and ask them to draw the dandelion for a classroom display.

6. Give each child photocopiable page 102 'Plant jigsaw' and a piece of A4 medium card. Explain that the pieces will fit together to make three different plants. Tell them to cut out all the shapes and stick the pieces onto the card to make the three different plants. When they have done this, they can colour each of the three plants and label the parts that they can see. They should be able to use 'flower', 'stem' and 'leaf'. Remind the children that the whole plants that they have been looking at have five parts: root, stem, leaf, flower and seed. Tell them that sometimes the flower and the seed are not on the plant at the same time, but this can happen with dandelions.

7. Give each child a sheet of medium-thickness white card and tell them to work on their own and draw their own imaginary plant with all the parts (including seeds and flowers at the same time). Tell them to think about the flower shape and colour and the shape of the leaves. Remind them to include the roots and that their made-up plant must have seeds and flowers on the plant at the same time.

8. When they have finished drawing their plant ask them to cut the card into approximately 12 pieces. Tell them to work in pairs and to fit together their partner's jigsaw. When they have done this ask them to identify each of the five parts – the root, stem, leaves, flower and seeds.

Introducing the new area of study

Learn some songs and rhymes about plants, such as 'Mary, Mary quite contrary', 'I had a little nut tree' and 'Lavender's blue'. Identify all the different plants that are mentioned in the songs. Explain to the children that they will be learning all about plants – how they grow, where they grow, what their needs are, and different types of plant around the school.

Differentiation
● Some children will need support when they are drawing their own plant and cutting it out to make a jigsaw.
● Challenge children to explain what they think the parts of the plants do. Ask them: *What are the roots for? What is the point of having brightly coloured flowers? Why do the plants make seeds? Why are the leaves of plants usually green?*

Science in the wider world

What plants are, what they look like and how they grow are important to know because we are so dependent on them. As the human population grows we will need more food, and unless scientists can invent another kind of food we will be still getting it from plants.

Review

The children could be assessed on their understanding of the names of the parts of plants and where each part is on the plant. They could also be assessed on how accurate their observational drawing of a dandelion is.

Resources
Pot plants or plants outside; media resource 'Parts of a flower (1)' on the CD-ROM; tulip or daffodil flowers (one for each pair of children); rulers; scissors; magnifying lenses; simple microscopes

Speaking scientifically
petal, stamen, stigma, pollen, similarities, differences

Lesson 2: Flowers

Introduction

Look at some pot plants, or flowers in the school grounds. Explain that flowers usually grow on stems and ask the children if they can show you any similarities or differences between the ones that they have seen. They will be different colours, some will have composite heads (like dandelions) and others will have a smaller number of petals. Some flowers have 'bits' (stamens) sticking up inside the petals; tell the children that they will be looking closely at the inside of a flower, including the sticking up 'bits', and doing lots of observational drawings.

It is important to tell them that it is against the law to pick nearly all wild flowers. Explain that the flowers they will be using were all from a shop and were all specially grown to be cut and then sold. They were never wild flowers.

Whole-class work

1. Show the class the media resource 'Parts of a flower (1)' on the CD-ROM and tell them the names of the main parts that they will be looking at: petals, stamens and stigma. Show them where the parts are. Give each pair of children their flower – a tulip or a daffodil. These have been chosen because the stamens, stigma and pollen can be seen easily. Of the two, the tulip is better, although it is sometimes more difficult to get hold of. Make sure that each child can see where the parts are and can recognise them in the real flower.

Individual work

2. Ask the children to count the stamens, petals and stigma and at the top of their paper write and complete these sentences:

- The flower has _____ petals.
- It has _____ stamens and _____ stigma.
- The pollen is on the _____.

3. Tell the children to observe the flower closely and then draw it.

4. Tell them to remove some of the petals and draw and label the stamens and stigma.

5. Ask them to look at the parts of the flower with the magnifying lens. They should take off a stamen and draw it under the lens and then label it. Ask: *Can you see the pollen? What colour is it?*

Differentiation
● Support children in identifying the parts of the flower and make sure that they use the correct spellings when they are carefully labelling their drawings. Microscope work is often difficult at first. If it helps, ask them to look at salt crystals or a feather before they try to see what pollen looks like.
● Challenge children to identify the parts of other flowers. Mixed bunches of flowers can be easily bought and contain many varieties with very different petals, stamens and stigma.

Science in the wider world

These parts – the stamens, petals, pollen and stigma – help plants reproduce. In the lessons on pollination, the children will see the link between identifying the different parts and how they fit into the plant's life cycle.

Review

Assess the children on whether they can identify the parts of a flower.

Objectives
● To know some differences and similarities between plants and animals.

Resources
Media resource 'What do seeds grow into?' on the CD-ROM; pictures of human babies and baby animals; adult plants; interactive activity 'Animal or plant?' on the CD-ROM; photocopiable page 103 'Plant quiz'; strips of paper A4 length and about 12cm wide (folded into three)

Speaking scientifically
plant, animal, root, stem, flower, seed, leaf, reproduce, similarities, differences

Lesson 3: Plants and animals

Introduction
Show the children pictures of human babies and baby animals such as foals, puppies and apes. Ask: *What do you think each baby animal will grow up to be? How do you know?*

Show the children the media resource 'What do seeds grow into?' on the CD-ROM. Can the guess what the seeds will grow into? Seeds – the plant's 'babies' – hardly ever look like the mature plant but baby animals nearly always look like their parents. This is one of the differences between plants and animals.

Whole-class work
1. Ask: *What other differences are there between plants and animals?* Complete this quickly; most children should be able to tell you that plants are often green, they don't move and half the plant (the root) lives in the ground.

2. Explore similarities and make sure that the children have remembered that both plants and animals need water and food and they both reproduce. You could use interactive activity 'Animal or plant?' on the CD-ROM to revise the similarities and differences.

3. Ask the children to imagine that they live in a scorching hot desert of rock and sand. Ask: *How would you help plants to survive there?* Stress the idea of them needing water and shade from the heat. Ask: *What about us?* We have similar needs – food, water and shelter.

4. Ask the children to imagine that it is freezing outside with snow, ice and hardly any sun. How would they help plants to survive? This time they would need warmth and light. Ask: *Would we have similar needs?*

Individual work
5. Ask the children to complete photocopiable page 103 'Plant quiz'. They should talk about their answers with other children on their table but all children should complete their own sheet.

Paired work
6. The children should work in pairs and use the paper that has been folded into three. The first child draws an animal head on the first fold of the paper and keeps it folded out of sight. The second child draws a plant body on the second fold, keeping it out of sight. The first child then draws human or animal legs on the third fold. It is important that each child can't see what the other child has drawn. Open up the folds and you will have a part-plant, part-animal impossible creature. Try a plant head, animal or human body and plant legs.

Differentiation
● Some children will need adult support reading the statements and deciding whether they are true or false.
● Challenge children to find plants that live in very cold regions and those that can grow in deserts.

Science in the wider world
This lesson reviews previous knowledge about the similarities and differences between plants and animals and stresses that a plant needs water, warmth, shelter and so on wherever it grows. This is a useful starting point for the chapter on habitats. It also begins to link seeds to growth of new plants, which relates directly to plant reproduction in later lessons.

Review
The children can be assessed on how accurately they complete the photocopiable sheet.

Objectives
● To understand the importance of pollination.

Resources
Pictures of seeds or real examples (acorns, conkers and sunflower seeds); media resource 'Parts of a flower (1)' on the CD-ROM; flowers containing lots of pollen – some flowers in supermarkets will be suitable, or in early spring look for catkins; small squares of black paper; simple microscopes; magnifying lenses; photocopiable page 104 'Pollination'; rulers; coloured pencils
(Note: although lilies contain lots of pollen, their pollen can stain, so may be best avoided.)

Speaking scientifically
stigma, stamen, pollen, pollination, insect

Lesson 1: Pollination of flowers (1)

Introduction
Show the children the seeds. Remind them what a conker, acorn and a sunflower seed are. Use the seeds to explain to the children that plants, such as sunflowers, grow and produce seeds so that a new plant can grow. The seeds grow into the new plant.

Whole-class work
1. Show the class the media resource 'Parts of a flower (1)' on the CD-ROM, and remind them of the names of the parts of the flower – the petals, the stamens and the stigma.

2. Explain to them that the pollen on the stamens has to reach the stigma. Pollen can go from the stamens to the stigma in the same flower, or it can go from the stamens of one flower to the stigma of another flower. This is what pollination is all about.

3. Talk to them about how they think that this might happen. Explain that some plants have pollen that blows from the stamens to the stigma.

4. Talk about how insects, especially bees, search for nectar on the flower's stigma, brush against the stamens so that pollen collects on their hairy legs, and then move to another flower and transfer the pollen onto the stigma there.

Group work
5. Give each table a few sheets of black paper, lenses, microscopes and flowers or catkins with plenty of pollen. Ask the children to shake the pollen from the flowers onto the black paper. Explain that this is what has to be transferred to the stigma to pollinate the flower so that seeds grow.

6. If possible, look at the pollen under the lenses and microscope. This can be difficult but it might be possible to observe the strange shapes of the pollen. If the children can see this, ask them to draw what the pollen looks like.

Individual work
7. Give each child photocopiable page 104 'Pollination' to complete. Explain that the photocopiable sheet shows pollen being blown between flowers, and flowers being pollinated by bees.

Differentiation
● Support those children who have difficulty matching the written labels to the pictures on the photocopiable sheet. Check that they understand what is happening and what the names of the parts of the flower are.
● Challenge children to look more closely at a range of different flowers and ask them why they think that the petals are brightly coloured or strange shapes – pictures of orchids are good examples. They will begin to understand that flowers have to attract insects so that they can be pollinated.

Science in the wider world
Insects are important for pollination and the children need to understand this so that as they grow older they can explore some of the problems that might occur if insects such as bees decline in numbers.

Review
Children can be assessed on how well they understand pollination and how well they can explain how it happens.

Objectives
● To understand the process of pollination and the life cycle of a common plant.

Resources
Media resource 'Parts of a flower (1)' on the CD-ROM; dandelions (or pictures of dandelions) at various stages of growth – including flowers and seed heads; photocopiable page 105 'Life cycle of a dandelion'; coloured pencils; glue; string; scissors

Speaking scientifically
flower, stamen, stigma, seed, seed head, pollen, pollinate, germinate

Introduction
Show the children the media resource 'Parts of a flower (1)' on the CD-ROM and remind them of the different parts. Ask them to imagine that they are bees. Ask: *What would you do if you saw the flower?* They should be able to explain that the bee goes for the nectar in the flower, collects pollen from the stamens on its hairy legs and body, then flies to another flower and does exactly the same thing – but also transfers pollen from its body and legs to the stigma of that flower. Remind them that if this doesn't happen the flower will not produce seeds and that it has to produce seeds so that a new plant can grow.

Whole-class work
1. Referring to the dandelions, tell the children about their life cycle, using pollination as the starting point.

2. The dandelion grows a bright yellow flower that bees and other insects are attracted to. Ask: *What happens next?* The children should be able to explain how pollination works.

3. Explain that the flower dies and the seeds grow. Ask them to tell you what a dandelion seed looks like and then show them the seed head – the typical dandelion clock. Ask: *What happens next?* They should know that the seeds float away.

4. Explain that the seed lands on the ground and then it germinates. This means that it is ready to grow, so a small root starts to go into the ground. Ask: *What happens next?* They should know that a new plant grows and the whole life cycle starts again.

Individual work
5. Give each child photocopiable page 105 'Life cycle of a dandelion'. Tell them that they can talk about it with the other children on their table but that they must finish the sheet themselves. They have to colour the pictures, cut them out and stick them in the correct order onto a piece of string, to make a 'hanging life cycle'.

Differentiation
● Support the children by giving them as much help as possible when they are completing the photocopiable sheet. It is not easy and some children will find the words difficult as well as the order in which they have to be arranged.
● Challenge children to find out how long the life cycle might take. What might happen if there were more insects? What might happen if there were fewer insects? What happens if the weather is cold or very dry?

Science in the wider world
Pollination, germination and growth depend on certain conditions and this lesson will lead to children considering the optimum conditions needed for this to happen. They will begin to understand the importance of insects, warmth, light and wet conditions, and space for plants to grow.

Review
The children can be assessed on how well they understand and can organise the life cycle into the correct order.

Objectives
● To begin to understand the wide variety of plants that grow in a small area.
● To know that the same kind of plant can have leaves that are different.

Resources
Pictures of British plants (trees, flowers, bushes, mosses, grasses); pictures or real examples of clover leaves; clover leaves (essential for this lesson); magnifying lenses; rulers; coloured pencils; sticky tape

Speaking scientifically
grouping, leaves, trees, flowers, bushes, moss, grass

Lesson 3: Plants in the local environment

Introduction
Show the children pictures of different kinds of plant and talk to them about what each one looks like and what it is called. Include flowering plants, trees, bushes, grasses and mosses.

Show them clover flowers and leaves and ask them how many leaves there are on each stalk. There are usually three. Talk about finding a four-leaved clover bringing good luck but that four-leaved clovers are difficult to find. Ask whether anyone has ever found one.

Whole-class work
1. If possible, take the children outside to look at real examples of the plants they were shown earlier. Count the trees, bushes and flowers in the school grounds and ask the children whether there are more flowers than bushes, more trees than bushes, or more trees than flowers. Is it possible to say what the most common group of plants is? If you have a large playing field, grass may well be the most common.

2. Take the children to several different places where clover grows and ask them to pick a few leaves from each place. It is important that they pick them from different places and from lots of different plants. Each child should take their leaves into the classroom and place them on their table.

Individual work
3. Give each child a magnifying lens and ask them to look closely at one clover leaf. Talk about the patterns on the leaves and ask them to describe the shapes. Ask them to choose a leaf, observe it closely and then draw it carefully to fill a piece of A4 paper.

4. Give each child another piece of paper and ask them to divide it into four equal boxes. Tell them that clover leaves don't always have the same pattern. Some will have the same pattern, especially if they are from the same plant or from the same part of the school grounds, but there should be several different and distinct patterns.

5. Ask the children to choose four leaves with different patterns and to use the magnifying lenses to look at them. They should draw each leaf in the separate box on the A4 drawing paper. The real leaves can be taped next to each drawing and then each sheet could be mounted as a display.

Differentiation
● Some children may need help in identifying four different patterns on the clover leaves and in neatly sticking the leaves onto their paper.
● Challenge children to find more than four different patterns. Ask them whether the patterns on the leaves of white or red clover are different or similar.

Science in the wider world
Clover is an important source of nectar for bees, and farmers often use it as green manure. They grow it and plough it into the soil to fertilise the next crop of plants.

Review
Assess the children's ability to find different patterns and draw them carefully and accurately.

Lesson 1: Plants for food (1)

Objectives
● To begin to understand that plants are important sources of food.
● To be able to identify which parts of different plants we eat.

Resources
A selection of vegetables and fruits (or pictures of them) including lettuce, sweetcorn, carrot, tomato, apple cabbage, broccoli, celery, parsnips, rice and an ear of wheat; a real pizza or a picture of one; a picture of spaghetti bolognaise; paper plates; photocopiable page 106 'Food from plants'; coloured crayons; interactive activity 'Food from plants' on the CD-ROM

Speaking scientifically
flower, root, seed, fruit, stem, leaf

Introduction
Ask the children to tell you what plants they think that they have eaten so far today and make a list. Leave the list where they can see it and tell them that they will look at it again later in the lesson.

Whole-class work
1. Tell the children that humans eat lots of plants – or parts of plants – every day. Show them each of the plants, or pictures of plants, you have collected and ask them to tell you whether it is a flower (broccoli), a root (carrot, parsnip), a seed (sweetcorn, wheat, rice), fruit (tomato, apple), stem (celery) or leaf (lettuce, cabbage). Remind the children that all plants have a life cycle that includes flowers and seeds, and that we can eat these parts of plants as well as roots, stems and leaves.

2. Talk about how we eat some of the plants. Lettuce can be in salads or sandwiches. Carrots can be cooked or grated and eaten raw. Apples can be eaten raw or cooked.

3. Explain that lots of the foods that we eat are difficult to identify. Show them a pizza, preferably a simple margherita, and ask them what they think it is made from. The base is wheat (seed); the topping is tomato (fruit). Show them the picture of spaghetti bolognaise and ask them what plants they think that is made from.

4. Look at the list of plants that the children have eaten today. Ask them to tell you which part of the plant each one was. Remind the children that plants provide food that is healthy and that we should really eat a lot of plants.

Individual work
5. Give each child photocopiable page 106 'Food from plants'. Tell them to discuss their answers with other children on their table but to complete the photocopiable sheet on their own or children can complete the interactive activity 'Food from plants' on the CD-ROM.

6. Give each child a paper plate each and ask them to draw a healthy plate full of plants that they would like to eat. Tell them to label each of the plants. These can be used as a display entitled 'Plants that we like to eat'.

Differentiation
● Support children who might find identifying the parts of the plants on the photocopiable sheet difficult. It is also important to make sure that the plates of food do really reflect what the children might eat.
● Challenge the children to look at the menu for school lunches, or a menu from a local restaurant and ask them to identify all the different plants included. Are there lots of plants, or very few? What are the most common?

Science in the wider world
The food we eat to stay healthy is important and we need to grow enough food for people in all parts of the world to eat. Plants are an important part of our diet.

Review
Assess the children on how well they can identify the types of food that we eat.

Objectives
● To learn that birds eat different types of seed.
● To understand that birds help to disperse seeds.

Resources
Pictures or DVDs of herbivores that eat a range of plants (cows, giraffes, elephants, hamsters and so on); pictures of parrots and of British birds such as sparrows; photocopiable page 107 'Which seeds do birds like best?'; a large bag of mixed birdseed; a plank of wood with four or five lids attached with strong weatherproof glue or nails

Speaking scientifically
herbivores, carnivores, sorting, groups, seed dispersal

Lesson 2: Plants for food (2)

Introduction
Remind the children that some animals are meat eaters (carnivores), some are plant eaters (herbivores) and some eat a mixture of both and are called omnivores. Ask the children what they think people are. Why do they think we are omnivores? What do we eat that proves it?

Ask the children which creatures they think eat the most seeds. It is probably us – humans – because we eat wheat and rice. Birds are also great seed eaters and help disperse seeds so that they can grow into new plants.

Whole-class work
1. Show the children the pictures of different herbivores and for each animal ask them what plants they think it likes to eat.

2. Show them pictures of birds such as parrots and house sparrows. Ask them what they think the birds eat. (They mainly eat different kinds of seeds.)

Group work
3. Give each table a pile of mixed birdseed and each child photocopiable page 107 'Which seeds do birds like best?' Ask each table to sort the birdseed into different types.

4. Show the plank to the children and explain that they will be placing a different type of seed in each lid. Ask the children where they think they should put the plank with the filled lids. It should be where they can see it but also where it is quiet and unlikely to be disturbed. Allow each group to put their seeds of each type into the lids and put the plank somewhere where it can stay undisturbed for a few days.

5. Ask the children to colour in their photocopiable sheet.

6. This experiment works best over a period of a few days. Check the lids regularly – perhaps twice a day and ask the children to complete their photocopiable sheet as soon as it is obvious that there are some seeds that birds like more than others.

Whole-class work
7. When all the seeds have gone from the trays and they have finished their photocopiable sheet, talk to the children about seed dispersal by animals and birds. Many plants have indigestible seeds that pass through birds and animals and start to grow. This can be good for the plants because the animals will leave their droppings a long way from the original plant so the ground won't get too overcrowded with one type of plant.

8. Some berries such as mistletoe and yew (both poisonous to humans) are sticky. When the birds wipe their beaks on branches or on the ground, the seeds fall off and grow again.

Differentiation
● Support some children who may find identifying the kinds of plants animals eat difficult.
● Challenge children to identify which types of garden birds are eating the most seeds.

Science in the wider world
Understanding that plants are just as important as food for animals and birds, as they are for us, is important.

Review
Assess the children on how well that they record their results on their photocopiable sheets.

Objectives
● To be able to identify the requirements for plant growth.

Resources
Pictures of a range of different plants or real examples, including water plants such as lilies, and cacti; photocopiable page 108 'What plants need'; coloured pencils

Speaking scientifically
basic needs, life cycle, growth, warmth, light, water, pollination

Lesson 3: Plants growing

Introduction
Talk to the children about what they need to stay alive. They will know that they have to eat food. Remind them that they eat solid food and have to drink water. They should also remember that they need light, air, space and shelter. All these things help them to keep warm.

Talk to the children briefly about the human life cycle – from babies, which grow into adults, who go on to have babies.

Whole-class work
1. Hold up a pot plant and ask: *What does this plant need to stay alive?* Remind the children that it needs food and ask them how they think the plant gets food. Explain to the children that it has to have water to help it grow in the soil. Show them a water plant, such as a lily, which can actually grow in water; and a cactus, which stores water.

2. We all need light, air and space to live and so do plants. They can't be too crowded together and the sun provides light for them to grow.

3. Show the children some pictures of plants growing in deserts, jungles, meadows and woods. Explain that there are very few plants that can grow in snow and ice and that frost in Britain kills a lot of plants. Talk about most plants needing to be warm in order to grow well.

4. All plants need to reproduce and this happens because of pollination, which they will all know about.

Group work
5. Give each child photocopiable page 108 'What plants need'. Explain that they are going to draw their own plant (have lots of pictures of plants or lots of pot plants around the room) and use each box to show how the plant stays alive and grows.

6. Ask for examples of what they will draw in each box. For example, in box 1, 'Water', they could draw their plant being watered using a watering can; in box 2, 'Light', the sun could be shining on their plant.

Differentiation
● Support children when they are drawing the illustrations on their photocopiable sheets and make sure that they are reminded about how pollination, which is a key part of the plant's life cycle, works.
● Challenge children to find out how plants survive in extreme conditions. Ask them to find out about cacti in deserts. How do they get water, for example?

Science in the wider world
Plants are essential for our food. For example, without wheat there would be no bread or pasta, so it is essential that we ensure plants have the right conditions to grow. Humans and plants are tied closely together.

Review
Children could be assessed on how well they can show the plant's four basic needs on their photocopiable sheets.

Objectives
● To understand that plants need water to grow.

Resources
Plastic cups; permanent markers; seed compost; cress seeds; watering cans; trays

Speaking scientifically
plant, grow, water, germinate

Lesson 1: Do plants need water?

Introduction
Ask: *Why do plants need water after seeds have been planted in soil?* The children should be able to tell you that they need water to sprout and grow. Ask: *How could we prove that this is true? How do you really know that plants need water?* They should be able to suggest that some seeds could be planted and that some could be watered and some not. Ask them what they think will happen if they performed this test. They should realise that the seeds that are not watered will not grow as well as the seeds that are watered regularly.

Paired work
1. Give two plastic cups to each pair of children and ask them to put their initials on the bottom and to draw a face on each cup using the permanent markers. Fill the cups almost to the brim with seed compost, sprinkle the cress seeds on top and then cover it with a thin layer of compost. Each pair should place one cup in a tray marked 'Water', which should be watered regularly. The other cup should be placed in a tray marked 'No water' and shouldn't be watered at all. Also write a large sign that says: 'Who will grow the most hair?'

2. Watch what happens over a period of seven to ten days. At the end of that time ask the children to write down what has happened to the cress seeds in each cup: the seeds without water should not have germinated; the cups that have been watered should look like faces with cress hair.

3. If there is time, ask them to draw what they can see.

Differentiation
● Some children will need support in planting their seeds and labelling their plastic cups. Some children will need support when they are writing about what has happened to each set of seeds.
● Challenge children to try growing different seeds in plastic cups with faces on them. They could use grass seeds or lettuce seeds. These both grow quickly and should produce spectacular 'hair'. Or challenge children to create the best-ever sandwich using their cress as one of the ingredients.

Science in the wider world
Understanding how to grow plants, and that once planted they need looking after, is important.

Review
Children can be assessed on their description of what happened to the seeds in each cup.

Objectives
● To understand that plants need warmth to grow.

Resources
Paper plates; waterproof glue; cotton wool; seed compost; cress seeds; small plant pots and trays to hold them; access to a fridge or somewhere cold

Speaking scientifically
planting, growing

Lesson 2: Do plants need warmth?

Introduction
Remind the children of the different needs of plants: water, warmth, food and so on. Ask: *How could we find out if it is true that plants need to be kept warm? What experiment could we do?* They should be able to suggest planting seeds and keeping some of them cold and some of them warm. The warm seeds should grow and the ones that are kept cold will either not grow at all or will grow badly.

Whole-class work
1. First of all plant something for fun. Give each pair of children a paper plate and tell them to glue cotton wool onto the plate in the shape of a face. They will need waterproof glue and two pieces of cotton wool for the eyes, one for the nose and a piece that can be shaped to look like a smile.

2. When the glue has set, drip water onto the cotton wool to make it wet. Tell the children to put lots of cress seeds onto the cotton wool. The seeds have to be pressed into the cotton wool as much as possible so that they won't wash off when the plates are watered. Ask the children where they think they should put the plates. (They should be put somewhere warm.)

3. Water the plates every day – or twice a day if necessary. Drip the water onto the cotton wool rather than pouring it on and after seven to ten days each plate should have a green smiling face.

Paired work
4. Now for the experiment. Each pair of children should plant two pots of cress seeds using the seed compost. One pot should go into a tray marked 'Cold' and one into a tray marked 'Warm'. Place the 'Warm' tray on a window sill or close to a radiator and the 'Cold' tray in the fridge or a similarly cold place. It is important to water both trays at least once each day.

5. Watch what happens over a period of seven to ten days. At the end of that time ask the children to write about what has happened to each set of plants. (The plants that have been watered and kept warm should have grown well; the plants that have been watered but kept cold will not have grown as tall, and may not have germinated.)

6. If there is time, ask the children to draw what they can see.

Differentiation
● Support those children who need help making their cotton-wool faces. They don't need too much cotton wool. Also support children who might need help writing their descriptions.
● Challenge children to use secondary sources to find out if there are any plants that can grow in really cold conditions.

Science in the wider world
Understanding the best conditions in which plants grow is important for growing crops for food, and also for maintaining habitats and biodiversity.

Review
Children can be assessed on how well they describe how well plants grow in warm and cold conditions.

Objectives
● To understand that seeds do not need light to grow but plants do.

Resources
Plant pots; trays; seed compost; cress seeds; a large cardboard box

Speaking scientifically
planting, germinating, growing

Lesson 3: Do plants need light?

Introduction

Remind the children of the two experiments that they have done so far. Talk about plants needing both warmth and water to grow. Ask: *What happened when your plants were not watered properly? What happened when your plants were watered but were kept cold? What do you think will happen if seeds are kept warm and well watered but in the dark? What test can we do to find out what happens to seeds in the dark?*

Paired work

1. Give each pair of children two pots, some compost and lots of cress seeds. Plant the cress seeds and place one pot in a tray marked 'Light' and the other pot in a tray marked 'Dark'. The trays should be placed somewhere warm and they should both be watered regularly with the same amount of water. The 'Dark' tray needs covering with a cardboard box or similar so that no light gets in.

2. After a few days the seeds in both trays should have started to germinate. This is because seeds do not need light to germinate. Remind the children that most seeds germinate in the dark and under the soil.

3. Watch what happens over a period of seven to ten days: although the seeds in the dark will have germinated, the plants will not be able to survive without light.

Individual work

4. The children should write responses to the following questions as a way of recording the results. If there is time they could draw what happens.

5. Describe what happened after a few days to both sets of seeds.

● What has happened to the seeds that have been kept warm, been watered regularly and allowed lots of light?
● What has happened to the seeds that have been kept warm, watered regularly and kept in the dark?

Differentiation
● Support children who might need help in writing their responses to the questions.
● Challenge children to allow a broad bean to grow in the dark and to draw what happens to it over a period of two to three weeks.

Science in the wider world

Understanding the best conditions in which plants grow is important for growing crops for food, and also for maintaining habitats and biodiversity.

Review

Children could be assessed on how accurate their responses to the questions are.

Objectives
● To identify some differences between seeds.

Resources
A sunflower seed or broad bean; pictures of the life cycle of a plant (such as the life cycle of a dandelion created in week 2, lesson 2); mixed birdseed; small pots; seed compost; paper already divided into two columns of five squares (one for each child); small sticky notes; coloured pencils; magnifying lenses; lots of adult volunteers

Speaking scientifically
life cycle, seeds, germination, plant, conditions

Lesson 1: Seeds

Introduction
Show the children a broad bean or a sunflower seed. Remind them that it is a seed from a plant. Ask them a series of questions that will help them to review a plant's life cycle: *What happens when the seed lands on the ground?* (It germinates.) *What happens next? After it flowers what happens? What happens to the seeds?* Refer to the dandelion life cycles created in week 2, lesson 2.

Whole-class work
1. Explain to the children that they are going to try to grow plants from birdseed and make observations about what happens. Ask them what they think they will have to do to make the seeds grow. They should understand that the seeds will have to be planted, watered and kept in a warm place.

2. Give out all the following resources to each table: small plant pots, trays to stand them in, seed compost and a handful of the mixed birdseed. Check that each handful of seed really is a mixture of different types of seed.

3. Each child needs their own sheet of paper that has been divided into ten squares, and a magnifying lens.

Group work
4. Tell the children to separate the seeds into different groups and put a sticky note next to each pile with a number for each. There shouldn't be more than five different types.

5. Ask each child to use the left-hand column of squares on their sheet of paper and use the magnifying lens to draw each of the numbered seeds. Number the squares with the same number that is on the sticky note.

6. Tell the children to plant the seeds in numbered pots. This is where lots of adult help will be useful because it is important to be able to match the numbered drawings of the seeds to the numbered pots.

7. Place the numbered pots in trays and water them daily until the plants grow. When the plants have grown the children should draw their numbered plants in the second column on their piece of paper, alongside the box with their numbered drawing of a seed. Ask: *Did the seeds look the same or different? Do the plants look the same or different? Does each plant look like the seed it grew from?*

Differentiation
● Some children will need adult help to separate the seeds, number them and draw each one in the correct box. They might also need help in planting and labelling the seeds with the same matching numbers.
● Challenge the children to identify the plants that have grown from the seeds. It should be possible to find sunflowers and some grasses.

Science in the wider world
The children need to know that plants grow from seeds and that they need to be helped to grow by providing them with the appropriate conditions.

Review
Children can be assessed on their seed drawings and how well they understand the plant's life cycle.

Objectives
● To learn how potatoes, pineapples and onions begin to grow.

Resources
Various seeds from previous lessons; pineapples – one per group (cut the tops off the pineapples leaving the green fleshy leaves and about 2cm of each pineapple); large potatoes and onions – one per group; plastic dishes; seed trays; jam jars; photocopiable page 109 'Pineapple, tuber and bulb'; rulers

Speaking scientifically
bulb, tuber

Lesson 2: Pineapple, tuber and bulb

Introduction
Show the children some of the different seeds that they have been using in previous lessons. Ask them to describe how they planted the seeds so that they would grow. Tell the children that they are going to look at how plants can be grown in other ways.

Whole-class work
1. Show the children the pineapples. Ask them what they are (some children may not have eaten fresh pineapple before). Tell them that you will be cutting the top off and seeing whether a new pineapple plant will grow from a piece of the plant.

2. Show the children the potatoes. Ask them what they are and whether they eat them. Tell them this is a tuber and that they will be watching to see if it will start growing into a new plant.

3. Show them the onions. Ask them what they are. Tell them it is a bulb and that they will watch how it grows. Ask them if they know any other bulbs. They might have seen daffodil or tulip bulbs.

4. Put a plastic dish, a jam jar and an onion, potato and pineapple on top of each table.

Group work
5. Give each child photocopiable page 109 'Pineapple, tuber and bulb'. Ask the children to place the top of their pineapple in the dish and add water so that the pineapple is resting in it. They can now draw this in the first empty box on their photocopiable sheet and then place the dish on a window sill. The water in the dish needs to be topped up regularly.

6. The children need to draw their potato on their sheet and then place it in a tray in a shady part of the classroom. There is no need for water.

7. Each group should fill a jam jar with water. The onion should fit into the top of the jam jar so that the root end of the bulb will just rest in the water. Ask them to draw this on their photocopiable sheet and then place the jam jar on the window sill. It must be kept topped up with water.

8. Observe the pineapple, potato and onion over a period of weeks: the potato will have shoots coming out of the tuber, called 'chits'; the pineapple and onion should start to grow roots and the tops will have green shoots. Ask the children to draw these changes. At the end of approximately three weeks, ask the children to complete their photocopiable sheets by writing down what has happened to each of their plants.

Differentiation
● Support any children who may need help in completing their photocopiable sheets.
● Challenge children to plant and grow their onions and potatoes outside, or in pots filled with compost.

Science in the wider world
Food crops are important and children need to know where food comes from and how it is grown.

Review
The children could be assessed on how well they complete the writing section of their photocopiable sheet.

Objectives
● To learn how plants 'drink'.

Resources
Three white carnations and a stick of celery for each group; five clear containers to hold water for each group; red and blue food colouring previously mixed with water; plastic aprons; magnifying lenses; photocopiable page 'How plants drink' from the CD-ROM

Speaking scientifically
stem, flower, roots

Lesson 3: How plants take in water

Introduction
Ask: *What happens if a plant isn't watered?* The children should know that it won't grow and will eventually die. Ask: *How do you think plants drink the water?* Make sure that they realise that plants take in water from their roots and that the whole of the plant needs water.

Whole-class work
1. Give each child photocopiable page 'How do plants drink?' from the CD-ROM. Refer to this and tell them that they are going to do an experiment to prove that plants draw up water.

2. Give each group a few sticks of celery (only one per group will be used for the experiment). Ask them to look at the cut stem through the magnifying lens. They should be able to see small holes. Tell them that most plant stems have these holes and this is how water travels through the plant.

Group work
3. Leave one stalk of celery with each group and give them two carnations with a whole stem and one with a stem that you have already split so that one half of the stem will go into one jar and one into the other. Make sure that all the stems are the same length and that they will fit into the containers without falling over.

4. Place each stem into the correct container: a carnation in each of the red and blue coloured water, the split stem carnation in both red and blue, and the celery stick in blue water. Place the containers where the children can see them and where they won't be knocked over.

5. Ask the children what they think will happen and tell them to record this on their photocopiable sheet.

6. During the day the plants will draw up the coloured water in a spectacular way: the petals of the carnations should take in some of the coloured water; the children should be able to see the blue food colouring in the capillary tubes of the celery.

7. Discuss what has happened and ask the children to record this on their photocopiable sheets.

Differentiation
● Support children who need help in recording accurately on their photocopiable sheets.
● Challenge children to try this experiment with other common flowers, such as dandelions, clovers or daffodils. They could also put a stick of celery in coloured water and measure how far the colour has come up the stem every 30 minutes.

Science in the wider world
Water, irrigation and knowing how to provide water to countries without much rainfall is important if there is going to be enough food for everyone.

Review
The children can be assessed on how well they can explain how plants 'drink' water.

Objectives
● To know some differences between deciduous and evergreen bushes and trees.

Resources
Trees and bushes in the school grounds or local area (including trees such as oak, sycamore and pine, and bushes such as holly and hawthorn); photos of twigs of oak, pine, holly and hawthorn (enough for one of each for every group of children); media resource 'Parts of a plant (1)' on the CD-ROM; coloured pencils

Speaking scientifically
trees, bushes, evergreen, deciduous, leaves

Lesson 1: Trees and bushes

Introduction
Take the children into the school grounds and ask them to find trees and bushes. Ask them to explain what the differences are. Trees are obviously bigger than bushes, but the children might look more closely and talk about trees having single large trunks and bushes having more branches and stems. If there are hedges at school, explain that hedges are made up of bushes growing close together. Discuss what we use trees for: talk about wood for furniture and for building houses and explain that paper can come from wood pulp.

Whole-class work
1. Show the children the media resource 'Parts of a plant (1)' on the CD-ROM and explain to them that both trees and bushes have the same parts. They all have roots, stems or trunks, leaves and flowers of some kind, but trees are much bigger and their flowers are sometimes difficult to see.

2. Show the children the pictures of twigs with oak leaves on and twigs with pine needles. (You man be able to use real twigs, if you are not using this book in season order.) Ask them to observe them carefully and describe the differences. They should see that the oak tree has larger leaves than the pine tree and that they are a different shape.

3. Talk to the children about deciduous and evergreen trees and explain that some trees like the oak are called 'deciduous' and lose all their leaves in the autumn. These leaves grow back in the spring when the weather gets warmer. Some trees, like the pine, don't lose all their leaves at the same time and still look green in the winter. They are called evergreen trees and often have dark green, tough, waxy leaves.

4. Ask the children to look at the pictures of holly and hawthorn twigs. (Avoid real examples of these, as holly berries are toxic and hawthorn twigs have very sharp spines.) Tell the children their names and that they are from bushes. Ask them which of the two is evergreen and why they think that it is. The holly should be the one they choose.

Individual work
5. Give each child two sheets of paper and ask them to divide each piece into two halves. On one sheet they should write the title 'Trees', then 'Oak' in one half and 'Pine' in the other half. On the second sheet the title is 'Bushes' and in one half 'Hawthorn' and 'Holly' in the other half.

6. Ask the children to draw each of the trees and bushes.

7. Underneath each drawing they should write whether that plant is evergreen or deciduous, and a plant or a bush. For example: 'The holly is an evergreen bush.'

> ### Differentiation
> ● Support children when they are writing their sentences.
> ● Challenge children to find the names of more deciduous and evergreen trees and bushes. Some children may want to use the word 'coniferous' rather than 'evergreen'.

Science in the wider world
Observing trees and bushes in their local area will be important when the children are exploring the habitats of different creatures.

Review
Children can be assessed on how accurate they are when labelling their drawings.

Objectives
● To know that there is a variety of leaf shapes in plants.

Resources
A large collection of leaves or pictures of leaves from trees and bushes that have a variety of shapes (including large ones such as chestnut, horse chestnut, sycamore, ash and oak as well as some smaller ones from bushes that have different shapes); large wax crayons; magnifying lenses

Speaking scientifically
leaf, trees, bush, vein

Lesson 2: Leaves

Introduction
Give each group of children some large sycamore leaves. Ask: *What do they look like? What shape are they?* Ask them to feel the leaves and describe what they feel like. They should realise that one side is much rougher than the other. Ask them what they think is on the rough side of the leaf. Explain what the veins do and tell them that the veins are similar to the capillaries they saw in their celery stem. Remind them about their experiment with the coloured water and tell them that trees are plants and work in exactly the same way as the carnations and celery stems.

Group work
1. Give each group a selection of leaves or pictures of leaves if no real examples are available and ask them to look at them carefully for a few minutes. Give them magnifying lenses and ask them to look closely at different parts of the leaves. Ask them to describe the shapes and to look at the similarities: *Which leaf has the most separate parts and which leaves are similar? Have some leaves got more veins than others? Are some darker or lighter green?*

2. Ask them to group the leaves and then to explain why they have grouped them in this way. Ask: *Are there other ways of grouping the leaves? How many different ways are there?*

3. Remind the children of the differences between deciduous trees that drop their leaves in the autumn and evergreen trees that don't drop all their leaves in autumn.

4. Ask them what kind of trees they think their leaves are from. They should tell you that they are all deciduous. Ask: *What would the leaves from evergreen trees look like?*

Individual work
5. Make leaf rubbings if leaves are available: give each child a large piece of drawing paper, and each group a collection of coloured pencils and a few large wax crayons. Show the children how to take a rubbing from a leaf. Tell them that they have to do some very detailed work on one leaf. If you are unable to make rubbings, skip straight to point 7.

6. Firstly, they must choose a leaf and take a rubbing from it. Remind them to do this from the rough side of the leaf.

7. Next, they must draw and colour the whole leaf.

8. Finally, they must choose two parts of their leaf. Using their magnifying lens, they should look very carefully and make two very detailed observational drawings.

9. The drawings could be part of a class display that shows the variety of plants in your school or local area.

Differentiation
● Most children should be able to complete this lesson without too much help. Some children will need support when they are completing their detailed drawings.
● Challenge children to use simple microscopes to look even more closely at parts of their leaves.

Science in the wider world
Using magnifying lenses and producing closely observed drawings is an important scientific skill.

Review
Children could be assessed on how well they produce their closely observed drawings using the magnifying lenses.

Objectives
● To understand the different ways that plants protect themselves.

Resources
A selection of nettle and holly leaves holly, rose and hawthorn twigs; cactus plants; magnifying lenses; magnified photos of nettle leaves

Speaking scientifically
thorns, spines, poison

Lesson 3: Plant protection

Introduction
Remind the children how important plants are as food. Talk to them about all the plants and fruits that we eat, from simple roots such as carrots, and fruits such as apples, to grasses and seeds, such as wheat and rice. Remind them of all the plants that animals eat, such as grasses for cows and horses, and leaves for elephants and giraffes. Tell them that animals need to eat plants to stay alive, but that some plants try to protect themselves.

Whole-class work
1. Tell the children that lots of plants have poisonous berries and seeds to stop them being eaten. Remind the children that they must never eat any berries or seeds that they don't recognise.

2. Show them the picture of the cactus and ask: *How is this plant trying to stop itself from being eaten? Why might these spikes act as protection?* (They could hurt the mouths of the animals that might try to eat it.)

3. Give each group pictures of rose and hawthorn twigs and talk about the spines on these plants.

4. Look at the nettles and talk about the tiny spines on the leaves that have poison in them that can irritate an animal's skin. Ask if any of the children have ever been stung by nettles and to describe their experiences.

Individual work
5. Ask the children to look at pictures of the twigs. Tell them to choose one of the twigs or the nettle and to draw what they can see.

6. If possible, find some magnified photos of nettle leaves. Ask the children to look carefully at the 'stings' on the nettle leaves and to draw what they see.

7. When the children have finished their drawings, ask them to complete these sentences:

- The rose and hawthorn bushes use their _____ to protect themselves.
- The cactus uses its _____ to protect itself.
- A nettle use its _____ to protect itself.

8. Give each child another piece of paper and tell them that they are going to design their own plant that is so well protected, it will never be eaten. Talk about the kind of protection that will be needed – spines, stings, poison and so on – and ask them to draw and label their made-up plant.

Differentiation
● Some children will need help in choosing the right words to complete the sentences. Some children may need support in creating their plant.
● Challenge children to look at individual pictures of spines from the cactus and rose twigs under the microscope and to draw and label them accurately.

Science in the wider world
Producing closely observed scientific drawings is an important scientific skill.

Review
The children can be assessed on how well they can complete the sentences and how well they can describe how their made-up plant can protect itself.

Objectives

● To assess whether the children understand the names of the main parts of plants.
● To assess whether the children understand the process of pollination.

Resources

Media resources 'Parts of a plant (2)' and 'Parts of a flower (2)' on the CD-ROM

Working scientifically

● Using their observations and ideas to suggest answers to questions.

Parts of plants and pollination

Revise

● Take the children outside into the school grounds or similar local area and look closely at a range of different plants.
● Look at the grass on the field. Ask: *What kind of plant is this?* Make sure the children understand the importance of grasses for our food, such as wheat and rice, as well as food for large numbers of animals, such as cows – which provide us with milk and cheese.
● When you see a tree, ask: *Is this tree deciduous or evergreen? How do you know?* They should understand that deciduous trees such as oaks have very different leaves from an evergreen tree such as pine or fir. Ask them to show you the tree's stem (its trunk) and to tell you which part of the tree helps to suck up the water from the ground. They should be aware that trees, like all other plants, have roots.
● Find some plants that are flowering and ask for volunteers to show everyone else where the petals are, what the stem looks like and which parts are the leaves.
● Back in the classroom show the children the media resource 'Parts of a plant (2)' on the CD-ROM. Point to each part in turn and ask them to tell you what its name is. Write down the names – stem, root, flower, leaf – where the children can see them.
● Show them the media resource 'Parts of a flower (2)'. Ask them to name all the parts and write these where the children can see them: petals, stamens, pollen and stigma.
● Remind the children that like all other living things plants have to reproduce. Ask them to tell you how pollination works. Try to encourage them to talk about the cyclical nature of pollination and plant growth: from flower to pollination by bees or wind, to seed production and seed dispersal, through to the seeds germinating and growing into a new plant and a new flower.

Assess

● Give each child three pieces of paper. On one piece of paper they should draw a plant and label all its parts accurately. Remind them to use the names that you have written down for them all to see.
● Ask them to use the second piece of paper to draw a picture of a flower and to label all the parts accurately.
● On the third piece of paper ask the children to complete these sentences:
  ● The part of the plant that grows underground is called the
  _____.
  ● The flower of a plant grows on the plant's _____.
  ● The main insect that pollinates flowers is a _____.
  ● Describe in a few words another way that pollination happens
  _____.
  ● Insects go to flowers to collect _____.
  ● Seeds fall on to the ground and _____ so that a new plant can grow.

Further practice

● Seed dispersal is fascinating, especially those seeds that are dispersed by the wind. Look closely at dandelion heads and at an individual dandelion seed. Draw one of the seeds, looking at it with a magnifying lens.
● Sycamore seeds can be thrown into the air. They float down like a helicopter with each wing of the seed spinning. Use the children's natural competitiveness to see whose seed stays in the air the longest.

Objectives
● To assess whether the children understand that plants are important sources of food for animals.
● To assess whether the children understand that plants are important sources of food for humans.

Resources
Pictures of a range of animals that eat plants; pictures of a range of plants that we eat (including roots, leaves, seeds and fruits); a large picture of a meal that includes meat, potatoes, carrots, peas and an apple pie; paper plates

Speaking scientifically
● Using their observations and ideas to suggest answers to questions.

Plants for food

Revise
● Remind the children that animals that eat plants are called herbivores. Ask them to tell you some animals that eat plants that live in Britain. They should know cows, sheep, horses and rabbits.
● Ask them to name animals from other countries that are herbivores. Show them some of the pictures. They will have seen zebras, giraffes and elephants on television.
● Ask: *What do birds eat?* They will recognise some common garden birds such as sparrows. Talk about sparrows eating a lot of seeds.
● Ask: *What do we eat?* Make a list of suggestions and show them pictures. Try to include lettuce, carrots, celery, peas, an ear of wheat, potatoes, tomatoes, and apples. Write down the name of each plant and then ask the children which part of the plant they eat. Write down their answers at the side of the name of the plant. For example, alongside lettuce write 'leaf'.
● Show the children the picture of the meal and ask them to tell you all the plants that are included. When they are describing the apple pie, make sure that the children understand that pastry is made from flour, which is made from wheat (a seed) and sugar, which is the stem of a plant (sugar cane) or the root (sugar beet).

Assess
● Give each child two paper plates. On the first one tell them that they have to draw a main course that they would like to eat. They have to label it with the types of plant that are in it. For example, if there are carrots they must write a label that says: 'carrot – root'. Their main course must have at least three plants in it.
● On the second plate they should draw and label a dessert that they would like to eat. Their dessert must have at least two plants in it.
● Give each child a piece of paper and ask them to complete the following:
  ● Name three animals that eat plants.
  ● Plant-eating animals are called _____.
  ● When birds eat seeds, some of the seeds pass through the bird and then

  _____.
  ● Name two plants that we eat that are roots.
  ● A lettuce is a _____.
  ● An apple is a _____.
  ● Write down the names of two other fruits that we eat.
  ● What do we eat that is made from wheat?

Further practice
● The most interesting thing for the children to do is to make something to eat that uses a variety of plants. The following suggestions will work if you have lots of adult volunteers, access to ovens and are aware of the safety of the children.
● Apple pies are fairly easy to make – so are pizzas or pasta dishes. Scones use flour, sugar and sultanas, and sandwiches are very versatile using wheat for the bread and all kinds of fruit and vegetables as fillings.

Objectives
● To understand that plants need light, warmth and water to grow properly.

Resources
A large broad bean seed and pictures of broad bean plants (it would be even better if the children had grown the actual plants themselves and could see them in the school grounds); pots; compost; trays; interactive activity 'What plants need' on the CD-ROM

Speaking scientifically
● Using their observations and ideas to suggest answers to questions.

What do plants need to grow?

Revise
● Show the children the broad bean seed and then the plant. Ask them to describe the seed and then to describe the plant. Ask: *How do you think that the seed went from being a seed to being a large green plant?*
● They should explain germination by describing that the seed falls to the ground – or is planted in the ground and covered in soil – then grows into a tiny plant and then gets bigger and bigger until it looks like the one in the picture, or the real plant in the school grounds.
● Remind them that plants need the same things that humans do if they are going to grow up to be strong and healthy. Ask: *What do we need to grow strong and healthy?* They should tell you that we need such things as food, water, warmth and shelter. Ask: *What do plants need – what does that tree/bush/dandelion need to grow strong and have flowers?* The answers should be similar.
● Show the children the pots, trays and compost that they have used in previous lessons. Ask them to tell you how they would grow the best bean plant ever. They should be able to tell you to place the seed in compost, to water it regularly and to keep the plant in the light and where it is warm. Ask them questions such as: *You wouldn't put it in the fridge then? Why not? Wouldn't it grow better in a dark box? Why not? Why bother watering it?*
● Use interactive activity 'What plants need' on the CD-ROM to reiterate quickly the key points from your discussion.

Assess
● Give each child a piece of paper. Tell them to draw the best bean plant ever – remind them how big the beanstalk grew in 'Jack and the beanstalk'.
● When they have drawn their bean they must write down why they think it will grow so well. They could say such things as: 'I water it every day'; 'It gets plenty of light'; 'I don't let it get cold'.
● On a second piece of paper ask the children to answer these questions:
  ● When a seed germinates what happens?
  ● What happens if you don't water seeds?
  ● What happens if you don't water a plant?
  ● Why shouldn't you keep a plant in the dark?
  ● If one seed is in the fridge and one is on the window sill, which one will grow best?

Further practice
● Looking after plants over a period of time is not easy and children need to know that growing food can be difficult. Create a proper vegetable bed in the school grounds and plant seeds at the right times in April and May. Use fast-growing crops that can be grown and eaten before the summer holiday. Broad beans might just be ready, but garlic and spring onions grow quickly, and different kinds of lettuce should do well. Plant them, nurture them, pick them and eat them.

Plant jigsaw

■ Cut out the pieces and stick them together to make three separate plants.

PHOTOCOPIABLE

Plant quiz

■ Read the sentences below and write 'True' or 'False'.

The flowers are usually below the ground. _____

Plants need water to grow. _____

Plants are often green. _____

The roots of a plant are usually above the ground. _____

Acorns are seeds and grow into oak trees. _____

Plants could run around the playground with us if they
wanted to. _____

Plant seeds always look like the adult, mature plant. _____

Plants need warmth and sunlight to grow. _____

I look a bit like a plant. _____

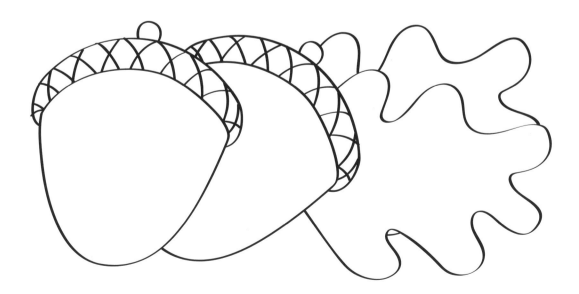

I can answer questions about plants correctly.

How did you do?

Pollination

■ Colour in the pictures.
■ Draw a line from each label to the correct place on the pictures.
Some labels may need more than one line.

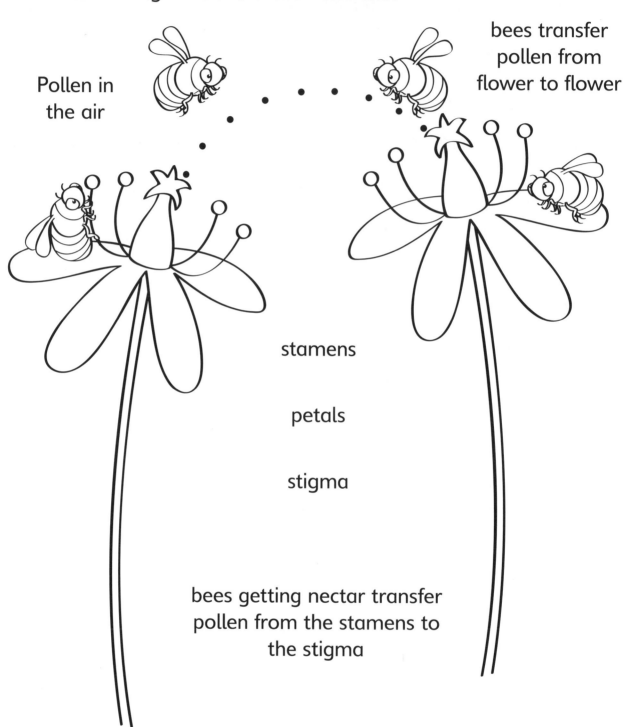

Pollen in
the air

bees transfer
pollen from
flower to flower

stamens

petals

stigma

bees getting nectar transfer
pollen from the stamens to
the stigma

I can describe how pollination happens.

How did you do?

PHOTOCOPIABLE

Life cycle of a dandelion

■ Colour in the pictures.
■ Cut out the pictures and the words.
■ Glue the correct word boxes onto the back of the correct picture and stick them onto a piece of hanging string in the right order – from top to bottom.

The flowers grow.	The seeds blow away.	The flowers die.	The new plant starts to grow.
The seed head forms.	Bees pollinate the flower.	A seed lands on the ground.	The seed germinates.

Name: _____   Date: _____

Food from plants

- Which part of each of these plants do we eat?
- Tick the correct box.

Plant	Leaves	Roots	Stem	Fruit	Seeds
wheat					
sweetcorn					
potatoes					
pears					
plums					
beetroot					
lettuce					
grapes					

I can identify which parts of a plant we can eat.

How did you do?

Which seeds do birds like best?

■ Place different types of seed outside where you can see them.
■ Watch carefully to find out which seeds the birds like best.
■ Complete the activities below.
■ Add labels to describe what the seeds in each lid look like. Do you know what kind of seeds they are?

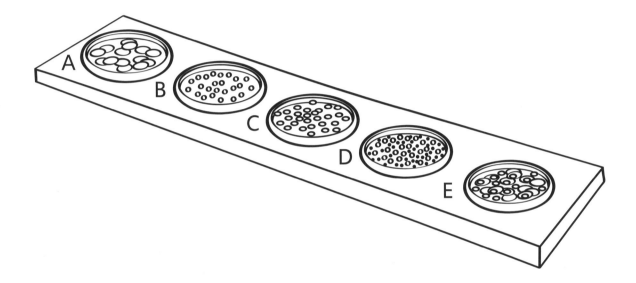

■ Which seeds did the birds like best? Record your results below.

_____

_____

_____

_____

I can record my observations.

How did you do?

PHOTOCOPIABLE

What plants need

■ Draw pictures in the boxes below to show what plants need.

Water	Light
Warmth	**Pollination**

I can identify what plants need to grow.

How did you do?

PHOTOCOPIABLE   ■SCHOLASTIC
www.scholastic.co.uk

Pineapple, tuber and bulb

■ Record how your plants grow in the spaces below.

Potato

What happened? _____

Onion

What happened? _____

Pineapple

What happened? _____

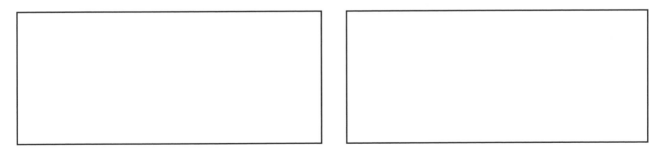

I can do record my observations.

How did you do?

Habitats

Expected prior learning

- Know the names of a range of different animals, birds and some insects and amphibians that live in their local environment.
- Know the names of some common plants, including trees, bushes and flowers.
- Understand that plants and animals need to live in certain conditions if they are to thrive and grow.
- Familiar with the kinds of foods eaten by a range of animals, birds and insects.

Overview of progression

After completing this chapter they should know about:

- the range of different local habitats
- animals needing different habitats
- the range of habitats in different parts of the world
- micro-habitats for a specific species (woodlice)
- the different birds using the school grounds
- how birds are suited to particular habitats
- simple food chains in local habitats
- food chains in other parts of the world.

Creative context

- This chapter provides opportunities for children to draw closely observed objects and to draw specific parts of animals and birds from secondary sources. There are also opportunities to design habitats.

Background knowledge

Habitats

- There are different habitats all around us for plants and animals, and many creatures and plants need special conditions in which to live. There are three very broad habitats of land, air and water, but each of these can be divided down into increasingly small and specific areas. For example, the children will be exploring the micro-habitat of the woodlouse. It is worth stressing how important each part of a habitat is, and how specialised habitats should be conserved.

Food chains

- All plants and animals are part of a food chain. Plants will always be at the bottom of a food chain and carnivores will be at the top.

Speaking scientifically

- Children may wish to know the names of a range of plants, birds and animals.
- They should also explore the idea of habitats that are totally different from their local ones. These will include deserts, rainforests and oceans.
- They will also need to remember the names of parts of plants, such as 'stem', 'root', 'flower', 'leaf' and so on.

Preparation

You will need to provide: pictures, books or DVDs of: common British animals, garden birds, insects, pondlife and river life; pictures, books or DVDs of: the Amazon rainforest, deserts, oceans and sea life, lobsters, crabs, shrimps and woodlice; resources to identify local wildlife; scrap materials; shoeboxes; magnifying lenses; containers for collecting minibeasts; small clear containers; three large sweet jars; compost; plants that will grow in moist, warm conditions, such as moss; plants that will grow in arid conditions, such as cacti or alpines; cress seeds; water spray; three large seed trays; sand; gravel; rocks; a large tank, rotting wood, moss, soil and dead leaves; mixed bird seed; chop sticks; salad servers; tweezers; a simple plan of the school grounds; nets; masking tape; spades; adult volunteers.

On the CD-ROM you will find: photocopiable page 'Deserts and rainforests'; interactive activities 'Desert and rainforests', 'Different habitats'

■ SCHOLASTIC

Chapter at a glance

Week	Lesson	Curriculum objectives	Objectives	Main activity	Working scientifically
1	1	• *To revise the objectives of Year 1.* • *To identify and name a variety of common animals.* • *To identify and name a variety of common plants.*	• To know that there is a wide range of plants and animals in the school grounds and in their own gardens. • To understand the word 'habitat'.	Discussing and identifying animals, birds, insects and plants that can be found in the school grounds. Drawing examples and completing sentences. Creating an imaginary creature and its habitat.	• Identifying and classifying. • Gathering and recording data.
	2	• Identify that most living things live in habitats to which they are suited.	• To understand that different habitats exist in the school grounds. • To learn that specific animals need specific habitats.	Discussing a range of habitats, such as air, water, in grass, under stones, in the soil. Drawing different habitats. Creating an imaginary creature and its habitat. Completing sentences about their imaginary creatures.	• Using their observations and ideas to suggest answers to questions.
	3	• Identify that most living things live in habitats to which they are suited.	• To understand that there are many different habitats needed by animals. • To learn that specific animals need specific habitats.	Discussing why specific common animals, such as sparrows, earthworms, rabbits, woodlice, need specific habitats. Creating an imaginary creature and its habitat. Completing sentences about habitats.	• Gathering and recording data to help in answering questions.
2	1	• Identify and name a variety of plants and animals in their habitats.	• To learn about the range of living things that live in deserts and rainforests.	Discussing deserts and rainforests using secondary sources. Completing sentences.	• *Use simple secondary sources to find answers.*
	2	• Identify and name a variety of plants and animals in their habitats.	• To learn about the range of living things that live in seas and rivers.	Discussing water habitats using secondary sources.	• *Use simple secondary sources to find answers.*
	3	• Identify and name a variety of plants and animals in their habitats, including micro-habitats.	• To find out about insects and invertebrates that live in micro-habitats.	Surveying micro-habitats in the school grounds.	• Gathering and recording data.
3	1	• Identify and name a variety of plants and animals in their habitats, including micro-habitats.	• To understand the characteristics of a woodlouse in its habitat.	Discussing woodlice – what they are and where they live. Drawing woodlice. Creating a habitat for woodlice.	• Observing closely.
	2	• Identify and name a variety of plants and animals in their habitats, including micro-habitats.	• To recognise which birds use the school grounds.	Observing birds and bird habitats in the school grounds. Painting habitats and the birds that live there.	• Gathering and recording data to help in answering questions.
	3	• Identify that most living things live in habitats to which they are suited and describe how different habitats provide for the basic needs of different kinds of animals and plants.	• To recognise that the birds in the school grounds eat different foods and have different shaped beaks.	Discussing the birds that are found in the grounds and researching how they feed. Drawing a bird in its habitat. Matching beaks to food types.	• *Use simple secondary sources to find answers.* • Identifying and classifying.

Chapter at a glance

Week	Lesson	Curriculum objectives	Objectives	Main activity	Working scientifically
4	1	• Identify that most living things live in habitats to which they are suited and describe how different habitats provide for the basic needs of different kinds of animals and plants.	• To know some different characteristics of plants living in the school grounds.	Discussing what plants need to grow – warmth, light, shade, water. Surveying plants growing in light and shady spaces. Drawing plants.	• Gathering and recording data. • Observing closely.
	2	• Identify that most living things live in habitats to which they are suited and describe how different habitats provide for the basic needs of different kinds of animals and plants, and how they depend on each other.	• To identify a variety of living things in and around a pond and begin to understand their interdependence.	Completing a pond survey. Discussing creatures and their needs using pictures where necessary. Drawing specific pond creatures.	• Observing closely. • Gathering and recording data.
	3	• Identify that most living things live in habitats to which they are suited and describe how different habitats provide for the basic needs of different kinds of animals and plants, and how they depend on each other.	• To be able to identify a range of local habitats. • To recognise the importance of protecting habitats.	Discussing what they found and where in the school grounds, including insects, birds, plants and pond creatures. Discussing how to protect habitats. Completing a chart.	• Observing closely. • Using their observations and ideas to suggest answers to questions.
5	1	• Describe how animals obtain their food from plants and other animals, using the idea of a simple food chain, and identify and name different sources of food.	• To know about food chains in familiar local habitats.	Discussing food chains that include birds, mammals and humans. Completing food chain diagrams.	• Using their observations and ideas to suggest answers to questions.
	2	• Describe how animals obtain their food from plants and other animals, using the idea of a simple food chain, and identify and name different sources of food.	• To understand food chains in less familiar habitats – rainforests.	Discussing food chains in rainforests. Researching rainforest food chains. Completing diagrams.	• Use simple secondary sources to find answers.
	3	• Describe how animals obtain their food from plants and other animals, using the idea of a simple food chain, and identify and name different sources of food.	• To understand food chains in less familiar habitats – oceans.	Discussing food chains in oceans. Researching ocean food chains. Completing food chain diagrams.	• Use simple secondary sources to find answers.
6	1	• Find out how the conditions affect the number and type(s) of animals and plants that live there.	• To understand that living creatures move through their habitats in different ways. • To know that creatures are able to adapt to the different habitats that they live in.	Discussing why different creatures live in specific habitats. Groups investigating worm movement. Drawing an earthworm and describing how it moves.	• Using their observations and ideas to suggest answers to questions. • Observing closely.
	2	• Find out how the conditions affect the number and type(s) of animals and plants that live there.	• To understand that living things need the correct conditions in order to survive.	Discussing habitats in the school grounds. Making suggestions for creating habitats.	• Using their observations and ideas to suggest answers to questions.
	3	• Find out how the conditions affect the number and type(s) of animals and plants that live there.	• To begin to understand how habitats can be created and preserved.	Discussing how the school grounds can be improved in order to increase the types and numbers of animals and plants living there. Designing and drawing plans for improving the school grounds.	• Gathering and recording data.
Assess and review					

Objectives
● To know that there is a wide range of plants and animals in the school grounds and in their own gardens.
● To understand the word 'habitat'.

Resources
Pictures of common British animals, birds and insects (birds such as blackbirds, sparrows and robins; butterflies such as cabbage whites and peacocks; bees and wasps; a common spider; woodlice; mammals such as rabbits, foxes, rats and mice; amphibians such as newts and frogs); Plasticine® (a golf-ball sized piece for each child); a shoebox or similar (one for each child); glue; scissors; a collection of scrap materials; access to the school grounds or similar local environment

Speaking scientifically
animal, bird, insect, habitat

Lesson 1: Living things

Previous knowledge
In Year 2 the children should be able to identify and name a variety of common animals and plants. They should also know the kinds of conditions that some of these creatures need to grow and develop. This lesson reviews some common animals, birds, insects and amphibians and begins to link them to the habitats in which they live.

Introduction
Encourage the children to identify the general characteristics of a range of creatures, and begin to classify them. For example, ask: *How do you know that a dog is a mammal?* They should suggest because it is warm-blooded, has fur and has babies. It also has four legs like many other mammals.

Ask them to describe what a bird is and what it looks like. Ask: *How is it different from a mammal?* Establish that it flies and has feathers but it does have two legs, just like we do.

Ask the children to describe a butterfly. Ask: *How is it similar to a bird? How many legs does it have? Do you remember what a butterfly's wings have covering them? How is a butterfly's life cycle different from a mammal's? How is it different from a bird's? What do you think butterflies eat?*

Frogs are amphibians. Ask: *What is an amphibian? What does a frog look like? What do tadpoles live in? How is a frog's life cycle different from a mammal's, and different from a bird's? How do frogs move? Is that different from how we move? Is it different from how a dog moves?*

Explain that all the creatures, including us, have to live somewhere. Use the word 'habitat' and tell them that all it really means is a place where something that is alive, like a plant or any kind of animal, insect and bird, can live, eat, breathe, have babies and grow up to be an adult.

Whole-class work
1. Show the children the pictures of British creatures that might be seen close to the school. As you show the children each picture ask: *What kind of habitat do you think that this creature lives in?* Make sure that the children are aware that rabbits live in burrows and need grass to feed on and that foxes live underground and eat rabbits. Discuss where non-flying insects as well as spiders and woodlice live: these will be much smaller 'micro-habitats'.

2. Take the children into the school grounds or other similar local environment and look for creatures that live there. Make a simple list of what you find. For non-flying insects, spiders and woodlice you may have to lift up rotting wood or old logs.

Group work
3. Ask the children to use the pictures from earlier in the lesson to draw three different creatures that they have seen. Tell them to produce beautiful pictures because these can be the start of a wall display called 'What we found in the school grounds'. Make sure that the children draw a wide variety of different creatures.

4. When they have finished their drawings, give each child a shoebox or similar and a piece of Plasticine® the size of a golf ball. Show them the scrap materials and odds and ends of junk and modelling materials. Tell them that you want them to create their own imaginary creature out of the Plasticine® and then to turn the shoebox into its habitat. The shoebox has to be where it lives, eats, breathes and has babies.

Checkpoint
● What different kinds of animal might you find in the school/your garden/your local area?
● What different kinds of plant might you find in the school/your garden/your local area?
● Can you think of an animal that lives in a very cold place?
● Can you think of an animal that lives in a very hot place?
● Can you think of a plant or animal that lives in water?

5. Tell them that they will have three lessons to create their creature and its environment. First of all, ask them to think about what kind of imaginary creature they are going to make. Is it going to be a mammal or an insect, an amphibian or a bird? If it is going to have wings they can make them out of scrap materials. Ask them to think about where their creature lives. For example, it might be a hole in the ground, under a log, in a tree or a field, or even underwater. Give them some paper and ask them to complete this sentence at the top (this will be returned to in the next lesson):

● My creature is a _____ and it lives in _____.

Introducing the new area of study

Show pictures of different habitats, including some that will be discussed later: a rainforest; the sea; a river; the arctic; a desert; the Moon. Ask the children to put up their hand if they would/definitely wouldn't like to live in each habitat. Ask them to give reasons for their answers. Explain that many creatures and plants live in all these places (though perhaps not the Moon!) and that they will be learning more about them in the following lessons.

Differentiation
● Some children will need support in choosing which animals to draw and make out of Plasticine®.
● Challenge children to do careful observational drawings and to label some of them. For example, insects could be labelled with legs and wings, but also with antennae and parts of the body such as head, thorax and abdomen.

Science in the wider world

The world population is growing and there is more and more demand for land to be used in different ways. Looking after the world's ecosystems to ensure we can grow food and making sure that habitats exist for creatures to live in is becoming more and more important.

Review

The children could be assessed on how well they can produce closely observed drawings and how imaginative and skilful they are in creating their imaginary creature and its habitat.

Objectives
- To understand that different habitats exist in the school grounds.
- To learn that specific animals need specific habitats.

Resources
Photocopiable page 135 'Habitats in the school grounds'; access to the school grounds; their imaginary creatures and shoeboxes; scrap materials; glue; scissors

Speaking scientifically
habitat, ground cover

Lesson 2: Different habitats

Introduction
Remind the children that certain creatures need different habitats. Go through some of the common creatures they saw when they were last in the school grounds, or that they might see in other places in the local environment. Say the name of each creature and ask them where it lives: for example, rabbits need holes in the ground and lots of grass and leafy plants; blackbirds need the air, bushes, and places where insects and worms are; butterflies need the air and plants with flowers; woodlice need dark, damp conditions under bricks and old wood.

Whole-class work
1. Give each child photocopiable page 135 'Habitats in the school grounds'. Read the headings to each of the sections and ask them to tell you what they think each one looks like. Remind them that up in the air, where birds and some insects fly, it is not empty. There are telephone wires and the tops of posts and the high branches of trees.

2. Take the children outside and show them examples of all five habitats. Ask them to look closely at each one and to look out for what is growing. Ask: *How can creatures shelter in different habitats? How can they move around? What food will they find to eat?*

Individual work
3. Using the photocopiable sheet, the children should record the habitats they have observed and discussed. They should use the left-hand space in each of the five sections for their drawings. The right-hand spaces will be completed next lesson.

4. Give the children their shoeboxes from the previous lesson. Remind them that they completed a sentence about their creature and its habitat. The children can carry on making their imaginary creature and its habitat. They could use pebbles, dried grasses and twigs from the school grounds. At a suitable point in the lesson ask them to describe where their animals lives, and write down where it shelters, underneath the sentence they wrote during the last lesson.

Differentiation
- Some children will need support when they are choosing what to draw in the sections on their photocopiable sheet. They might also need support when they are writing descriptions of their invented habitat.
- Challenge children to make more of their shoebox habitats and to write detailed descriptions of it.

Science in the wider world
The world population is growing and there is more demand for land to be used in different ways. Looking after the world's ecosystems to ensure we can grow food and making sure that habitats exist for creatures to live in is becoming more and more important.

Review
The children could be assessed on how well they draw each of their five habitats on their photocopiable sheets. They could also be asked to tell you about what they have drawn under each heading.

Objectives
• To understand that there are many different habitats needed by animals.
• To learn that specific animals need specific habitats.

Resources
Pictures of common British animals, insects and birds from lesson 1; photocopiable sheets from the previous lesson; magnifying lenses; their imaginary creatures and shoeboxes; scraps of materials; scissors; glue; containers for collecting minibeasts

Speaking scientifically
habitat

Lesson 3: Animal homes

Introduction
Give each child photocopiable page 135 'Habitats in the school grounds' from the previous lesson and remind them of the five different habitats that they have drawn. Ask for volunteers to describe each of the five habitats. Show the children some of the creatures that they saw in the school grounds, as well as some animals, such as rabbits and earthworms, which they might not have seen but are still common. Their pictures from lesson 1 should still be on display.

Whole-class work
1. Take the class outside and look in turn at each of the habitats. Look in the air and at the tops of trees and on any telephone wires. If there are birds and insects try to identify them.

2. Look at the trees and bushes. There should be birds such as sparrows, but there might also be caterpillars and other insects. If there are, take them carefully back into the classroom.

3. The grass and flowers should have bees and possibly butterflies. Under the ground will be worms. Dig up a small patch of earth and take any creatures, such as worms, back into the classroom.

4. Carefully lift up any rotting logs or stones and collect any spiders or beetles.

5. If you have a pond, look out for frogs and newts but don't do a detailed search as this is something that will be done in a later lesson.

Individual work
6. Use magnifying glasses to look at any creatures that have been collected and tell the children to draw them in the space next to the appropriate habitat on their photocopiable sheets. Use pictures to help them produce accurate drawings. Don't forget to take the creatures that have been collected back to exactly where they were found. They should understand that specific creatures need specific habitats and if they aren't retuned to the correct habitat then they won't be able to eat and grow.

7. Give the children time to finish their imaginary creature's habitat. Ask them to write down what their creature eats, and how it moves around its habitat, on their sheet of paper from the previous lessons.

8. Ask some children to show the class their creatures in their habitat and to talk about how they live, what they eat and how they move.

Differentiation
• Support children in matching the creatures they saw in the school grounds or the creatures in the pictures to the five habitats on their photocopiable sheets. Some children may need help in writing about their imaginary creature.
• Challenge children to use stronger lenses or microscopes to look more carefully at some of the creatures that were collected.

Science in the wider world
Creatures large and small need specific habitats. If we preserve the habitat we preserve the creatures. If we destroy the habitats we destroy the creatures.

Review
Children can be assessed on how accurately they identify the creatures they draw on their photocopiable sheets.

Objectives
● To learn about the range of living things that live in deserts and rainforests.

Resources
Pictures/books/DVDs of the Amazon rainforest and deserts; photocopiable page 'Deserts and rainforests' from the CD-ROM; interactive activity 'Deserts and rainforests' on the CD-ROM; three large sweet jars or similar; compost; plants (including mosses) that will grow in moist, warm conditions; cress seeds; water spray; three large trays; sand; gravel and rocks; a selection of cacti or alpine plants that will grow in arid conditions

Speaking scientifically
hot, wet, dry, rainforest, desert

Lesson 1: Deserts and rainforests

Introduction
Ask the children to imagine that the school has suddenly changed into a rainforest. Ask: *What animals might you see and hear?* At this stage don't give them any facts about rainforests. Now tell the children that suddenly the school has turned into a desert. Ask: *What might you see and hear now?*

Whole-class work
1. Show the children books, pictures, or wildlife DVDs about rainforests. Make sure that they understand that a rainforest is hot and wet with huge trees, and plants with very large leaves. Talk about the wide range of plants, insects and animals. Explain that many habitats are in the tree canopy because the forest floor is dark. Contrast your local environment with the rainforest.

2. Look at similar secondary sources about the desert and talk about the heat and the dryness. There is very little water in a desert and anything that lives there has to be able to go for long periods without water. Talk about some of the animals and plants that they can see in the pictures.

Individual work
3. Ask the children to complete the sentences and answer the questions about deserts and rainforests on the photocopiable page 'Deserts and rainforests' from the CD-ROM or to complete the interactive activity 'Deserts and rainforests' on the CD-ROM.

Group work
4. Give each group a large sweet jar, some compost and a few plants and cress seeds. Tell them that it is possible to create a mini rainforest in the jar. All they have to do is lay the jar on its side, put in some compost and a few seeds and plants, and spray the plants and seeds with the water. The sweet jar can be left on a hot window sill and sprayed regularly to keep the habitat warm and wet. The plants should grow lush and green and the inside of the jars should be wet and warm with lots of condensation.

5. Give a tray to each group and some sand, grit, a few rocks and cacti. (If you don't want to risk cacti spikes, there are all kinds of alpine plants that need dry conditions.) Each group can make a desert and place this on the window sill or somewhere warm. Don't water the desert at all.

6. Over a period of a few weeks, look at both the habitats the children have made and ask them to tell you some of the differences between them.

Differentiation
● Support children who find completing the writing difficult.
● Challenge children to write down the names of as many animals that live in the two habitats as possible. They could also look on a globe or in an atlas to try and find where deserts and rainforests are.

Science in the wider world
Conservation of habitats, such as deserts and rainforests, is important for biodiversity and slowing down global warming.

Review
The children can be assessed on how well they complete the writing task and how well they understand the differences between deserts and rainforests.

Objectives
● To learn about the range of living things that live in seas and rivers.

Resources
Books, pictures, DVDs/ wildlife programmes showing life on British rivers and in oceans; coloured pencils; art paper; paints

Speaking scientifically
fish, mammal, reptile, shellfish, seaweed

Lesson 2: Rivers and seas

Introduction
Talk to the children about rivers and lakes, and seas and oceans. Rivers and lakes are largely fresh water and seas and oceans are salt water. Explain that we drink fresh water and that all the birds, insects, plants and mammals around the school need fresh water as part of their food.

Whole-class work
1. Show the children secondary sources, such as pictures, books and DVDs, about British rivers and the living things that use them as their habitats, such as voles and otters. Show them dragonflies, which grow in the river before turning into insects that fly close to water to hunt and lay their eggs. Tell them that fish such as pike and trout live under the water, and birds such as kingfishers need a river for their food.

2. Show similar secondary sources about oceans and the living things that inhabit them, such as whales, seals, sea lions and dolphins. Explain that some whales are the largest living creatures on earth. Talk about plankton, which whales live on. Show them shellfish, which grow at the edges of the sea; crocodiles, which move between the land and the water; fish, such as sharks and mackerel; and jellyfish, which float through the water. Some birds, such as penguins, use the sea to catch their food, and plants such as seaweed live their whole lives in water.

3. Ask the children questions such as: *How do fish move? What are the main differences between a penguin and a sparrow? What do sharks eat?*

Individual work
4. Ask the children to write down the names of three creatures that live in fresh water (rivers and lakes) and three creatures that live in salt water (the seas and oceans).

5. Ask the children to draw and label one creature from a river and one from the sea.

6. Tell the children that they are going to make a huge wall display called 'Under the sea'. Mount large sheets of blue paper on a display board. Make sure that each table has pictures of creatures and plants that live in the sea and that each child has a piece of good-quality art paper and paints. Each child should paint one creature that lives in the sea and cut it out carefully. Each picture can be stuck onto the display until there is a large crowded underwater collage.

Differentiation
● Support children who may need help in writing the names of some of the creatures. Some children may also need help in choosing an appropriate creature to paint.
● Challenge children to look at the life cycles of some of the creatures, such as whales, which travel huge distances, and penguins, which leave their mates and eggs for weeks at a time when they go to the sea for food.

Science in the wider world
Creatures such as whales are very dependent on there being huge quantities of plankton. There is a balance of nature that has to exist or many water-based species will not survive.

Review
Children can be assessed on their written lists of animals that live in fresh and salt water.

Objectives
● To find out about insects and invertebrates that live in micro-habitats.

Resources
Photocopiable page 136 'Minibeast sampling'; books and pictures of minibeasts; small containers to collect minibeasts in (three for each pair of children marked 'A' for rocky, 'B' for grassy and 'C' for dark and damp); magnifying lenses; pencils; access to areas of the school grounds that are rocky (stony), grassy, and dark and damp (it is important that you have already found these areas so that the children can be told where to look)

Speaking scientifically
minibeast, grass, soil, rocks

Lesson 3: What can you do in the sunshine?

Introduction
Explain to the children that they will be going out to look for minibeasts. These are small creatures that are difficult to see but that still live in certain places – in specific habitats. Explain that they might have go out to look more than once because they might not find any minibeasts. Remind them to take care because the tiny creatures they find are fragile and tell them that they must put the creatures back exactly where they found them because that is where they live: that is their habitat.

Whole-class/paired work
1. Show the children some of the books and DVDs about minibeasts and look closely at some of the common ones that you are more likely to find. Ask: *Where might you find worms? How do you think worms move?* Remind them that spiders aren't insects. Ask: *How many legs does a spider have? How many legs does an insect have?* Look at ladybirds: there are lots of types, with different numbers of spots. Ladybirds eat aphids, which are pests, so gardeners like to see ladybirds around.

2. Give each child photocopiable page 136 'Minibeast sampling' and tell them that they will be working with a partner. Give each pair of children a magnifying glass and the three labelled containers.

3. Explain to the children that they will be going to look for minibeasts in three specific habitats. Show them the letters on their containers and tell them that A is a rocky place, B is a grassy place and C is a damp and dark place. They have to look for minibeasts in these three areas, carefully put them in the correct containers and bring them back to the classroom.

4. Take the children outside to work in pairs, preferably with support from other adults.

Individual work
5. When the children come back to the classroom, ask them to record the information they have gathered on their photocopiable sheets. They will need to count the minibeasts they have found and identify them using the books, pictures and adult help. They will also need to count them and use their magnifying lenses to look closely at each minibeast as they are drawing it.

6. Can they tell what the most common minibeast is? Is there a favourite habitat?

Differentiation
● Some children will need help to find minibeasts and will need support identifying what they have found and completing their photocopiable sheets.
● Challenge children to look at other habitats: in dry places, wet places, under wood or under rocks, under bushes and in flower beds.

Science in the wider world
It is important for children to be aware that gardens and school grounds have habitats for all kinds of creatures.

Review
Assess the children on how well they complete their photocopiable sheets. Have they identified what they have found accurately?

Objectives
● To understand the characteristics of a woodlouse in its habitat.

Resources
Pictures of crustaceans (such as lobsters, crabs and shrimps); a large picture of a woodlouse; a large tank; rotting wood; moss; a small quantity of earth; dead leaves; magnifying lenses; one clear container for each child; access to the school grounds

Speaking scientifically
habitat, crustacean, herbivore

Lesson 1: Woodlice

Introduction
Show the children the pictures of crabs, lobsters and shrimps. Ask: *Where do you think these creatures live? Are they mammals, insects, birds, amphibians or something else?* Explain that they are crustaceans and there is one crustacean that they can find in the school grounds. Can the children guess what it is? Show them a large picture of a woodlouse.

Whole-class work
1. Most of the children will have seen woodlice when they were sampling minibeasts. Explain that they have flexible bodies (some can curl up into a ball); they live in dark, damp places; they are herbivores and eat dead leaves and plants; they are about 1cm long. Ask: *Where might we find woodlice in the school?*

2. Show the children the tank and ask them what they will need to put into the tank if they are going to look after some woodlice for a few days. Make sure they understand that they will have to make a dark, damp habitat with lots of dead leaves, dead wood and other rotting vegetation.

3. Take the children outside to find some woodlice. Let them look for likely places but make sure that you are able to show them where you know that woodlice are likely to be. They need to collect one or two in their small, clear containers.

Group work
4. When the children come back to the classroom ask them to use their magnifying lenses to help them to create a detailed observational drawing of the woodlouse. They will also need to complete the following sentences:

- I am a woodlouse and I like to eat _____.
- My favourite place to live is _____.
- I am not an insect, a bird or a mammal. I am a _____.

5. As the children are completing their drawings allow them to take turns in helping you to create a habitat for woodlice to live in.

6. Put all the woodlice that have been collected into their new home and observe them over a period of a few days before putting them back where they came from in the school grounds.

Differentiation
● Some children will need support in completing the sentences; make sure they can see some of the key words that they will need.
● Challenge children to find out more about crustaceans such as lobsters and crabs. They could also use secondary sources to find out about the life cycle of a woodlouse.

Science in the wider world
Habitats don't have to be huge like rainforests and deserts. Even the smallest habitats support creatures and need to be looked after.

Review
Children can be assessed on how well they can complete the written sentences.

Objectives
● To recognise which birds use the school grounds.

Resources
Books, pictures and wildlife DVDs of common garden birds; mixed birdseed; coloured pencils; paint; access to school grounds

Speaking scientifically
bird, habitat

Introduction
Tell the children that they are going to produce a large display of birds in the local environment Talk about the different kinds of environments that are close to the school. Remind them that birds fly but also need trees, bushes and open fields. In ponds in the countryside they will see water birds such as mallards, swans and Canada geese.

Whole-class work
1. Go out into the grounds and look at bird habitats rather than specific birds. Remind the children that some birds use bushes and trees to find their food and to build nests.

2. Ask the children why birds need to build nests and remind them of the life cycle of all birds. Talk to them about the kinds of bird that nest in bushes (blackbirds and robins); the kinds of bird that need buildings for their nests (starlings and house sparrows); those that need water (ducks, swans and geese); and those that nest in trees (crows and rooks). Most birds use materials from their habitats to build their nests, such as pieces of grass, moss, twigs and so on.

3. Divide the children into groups and ask them to sit quietly for a few minutes and look at what the birds are doing. They should see them flying but they should also see them landing in bushes, on the ground and in trees. If they are lucky some might be feeding from the seeds that have been put down or looking for worms in the grass.

Group work
4. Ask each table to use pieces of art paper, paints and/or coloured pencils to draw bird habitats. Organise it so one group paints trees, one bushes and so on. Mount these on a large display board. These are the habitats.

5. Make sure that each table has a selection of books and pictures of common birds that they have seen. Tell them to choose a bird each and then draw and paint it. They should then cut their birds out to be mounted in the correct place on the habitats display.

Differentiation
● Some children will need support in identifying some of the birds as well as matching them to their habitats.
● Challenge children to look at rarer birds in very different habitats. Ask them to find out about ospreys, grouse, puffins and even golden eagles. What do these birds eat and where do they live?

Science in the wider world
Many common birds are in decline and are becoming less common. It is important that we try to preserve their habitats and that children begin to recognise how important this is.

Review
Children can be assessed on their understanding of how specific birds can be linked to their food, their habitat and how they use the habitat for making nests and collecting the food they need.

Objectives
● To recognise that the birds in the school grounds eat different foods and have different shaped beaks.

Resources
Photocopiable page 137 'Birds' beaks'; pictures and books of common birds; birdseed (mixed variety); chopsticks; salad tongs; tweezers; rulers; coloured crayons

Speaking scientifically
seed, beak

Lesson 3: Adapting to habitats

Introduction
If possible, put out lots of birdseed close to the classroom for a few weeks before this lesson.

Talk to the children about the kinds of birds that they see in the grounds and in the local environment; write down some of their names. Talk about birds that they might have seen at weekends, such as buzzards, or ducks in local ponds; discuss what they might eat.

Whole-class work
1. Remind the children about birds needing the right habitat. Ask: *Where do birds go for food?* Some birds eat from the ground and some from bushes; some birds eat out of water and some catch other birds and small mammals. They each need a habitat with the right kind of food in it. Talk about what birds eat, such as seeds, insects, worms, water plants and other creatures.

2. Give each child photocopiable page 137 'Bird's beaks'. Look at each bird in turn and ask them to identify what this bird eats. Link the shape of the beak to the kind of food: for example, a thin, dagger-like beak for eating small insects; a sharp, tearing beak for eating other small creatures.

3. Ask the children what kind of habitat a seed eater needs. Birds that eat seeds need to be close to plants and bushes that have flowers and seeds; birds that eat insects need to be close to where insects live.

Individual work
4. Tell the children to complete their photocopiable sheet. When they have finished, ask them to choose a bird that they have seen and draw a picture of it eating food in its normal habitat. Underneath the picture they should write:

- My bird is a _____.
- It eats _____ and its habitat is _____.

5. While the children are working, ask two or three at a time to try to use the tweezers, chopsticks and salad tongs to pick up some of the seeds. It will show them that the shape of a bird's beak is important: tweezers can only pick up single seeds and chopsticks a few more, but salad tongs should be able to pick up quite a lot of seeds.

Differentiation
● Support those children who need help completing their photocopiable sheets and their writing task, and make sure that their choice of bird is appropriate for their drawing.
● Challenge children to find more links between more common birds – what they eat and their habitat; blackbirds, for example, eat worms that they find in grass and soil. Peregrine falcons are interesting and children will be fascinated when they find out how fast they can fly.

Science in the wider world
Birds are all around us but many garden birds are in decline. The more we know about where they live and what they eat, the more we will know about preserving the habitats they need.

Review
Children can be assessed on how accurately they can complete their photocopiable sheets and how well they finish the sentences underneath their drawings.

■SCHOLASTIC

Objectives
● To know some different characteristics of plants living in the school grounds.

Resources
Coloured pencils; clipboards; copies of a plan of the school grounds (a very simple plan with areas of the ground marked with shady spots, sunny flower beds, bushes, grass, rough ground); photocopiable page 138 'Where plants live'; access to the school grounds

Speaking scientifically
life cycle, pollination, germination, habitat

Lesson 1: Plant habitats

Introduction
Remind the children that plants need food, which comes from the soil and from water, and that they need appropriate warmth and light. They also need to be pollinated so that they can produce seeds to germinate and grow into new plants. This means that plants have to grow in a habitat that will give them food, warmth and light, as well as insects for pollination. Without the correct habitat the plants will not grow. It will be useful to go through a plant's life cycle and make it clear to the children that the insects that pollinate the flowers also have to have the correct habitat or there won't be enough of them to pollinate all the flowers – and if they don't pollinate the flowers there won't be any flowers growing either.

Whole-class work
1. Show the children a plan of the school and make sure that they understand it. Ask: *Where are the shady habitats? Where are the sunny flower beds? Where are the bushes?*

2. Give each child a selection of coloured pencils, some paper and a board to rest their paper on. Explain that they are going to choose a plant to look at and carefully draw. As soon as they have chosen their plant they need to write where its habitat is. For example, if they choose a daisy, they will write on their paper: 'A daisy from the grass'.

3. The plan of the school could be mounted on a display board and the drawings mounted around it. The drawings could be linked to the correct habitat with cotton or embroidery thread.

Individual work
4. Talk to the children about where they found their plants. Ask volunteers to explain what their plants were and where they found them. If some were found in strange places, like on the edge of the pond or growing in the gaps in paving stones, talk about the ability of plants to grow almost anywhere. Some plants might not be familiar to the children so talk to them about mosses and fungi. Ask them where they have seen mosses and fungi in the school grounds. Explain that although fungi look like plants, they are actually something different.

5. Give each child photocopiable page 138 'Where plants live' and ask them to complete it. Some of the plants can be easily matched to their habitats but some are more difficult.

Differentiation
● Support children who will need help in explaining where their plant's habitat is, or in identifying their plant.
● Challenge children to look at moss under a magnifying lens and draw what they see.

Science in the wider world
Humans and most animals need plants for food so it is important that we recognise their habitats and make sure that we try to preserve them.

Review
Children can be assessed on how well they identify the plant they draw and how they know where its habitat is.

Objectives
● To identify a variety of living things in and around a pond and begin to understand their interdependence.

Resources
Nets and containers; books and pictures of pond life; magnifying lenses; coloured pencils; photocopiable page 139 'Pond life'; rulers; access to a pond

Speaking scientifically
pond, water, amphibian, habitat

Lesson 2: Ponds

Introduction
Remind the children that frogs need to live close to water. Discuss their life cycle and that tadpoles need a water habitat but adult frogs need warm, damp conditions close to water. Ask the children what other creatures they think live in and near a pond. They should know that ducks and swans live on and around ponds as well as fish, insects such as dragonflies, and plants.

Whole-class work
1. The children need clear containers, nets and magnifying lenses. Take them out to the school pond or one that is close enough to school for them to be able to bring samples of creatures back into the classroom and then return them to the pond safely and quickly. Take some of the books out with you to help identify the creatures that the children find.

2. First of all, look around the pond at insects and plants that need wet conditions. Use the nets to dip into the pond and collect different creatures that live in the water. You might find dragonfly larvae, small fish such as sticklebacks, and water beetles and snails. Keep them carefully in the containers.

Group work
3. Back in the classroom tell the children to look carefully at what they have found and to try to identify what each creature is using the books and pictures.

4. Ask them to observe one creature closely, using the magnifying lens, and then draw it. Information about the pond could be recorded as a class display.

5. Give each child photocopiable page 139 'Pond life'. Talk about each of the creatures and plants. This is a good opportunity to remind them of the kinds of food different creatures eat. For example, tadpoles eat plants, and fish and newts eat the tadpoles.

6. Tell them to colour in the creatures and plants on the sheet and then identify each creature's home or habitat by drawing a line with their ruler.

Differentiation
● Support children who find it difficult to use the books and pictures to identify the creatures they have found. Some children will need support matching the creatures and plants on their sheets to their habitats.
● Challenge children to use the secondary sources to look more closely at some of the creatures in ponds. For example, can they find out what a dragonfly larva eats? How is this different from the adult dragonfly? What about pond skaters – how can they skate along on the top of the water without sinking? How do sticklebacks look after their eggs?

Science in the wider world
Ponds are homes to a wide variety of creatures that wouldn't exist without the pond. Conservation and protecting ponds is important.

Review
Children can be assessed on how well they complete their photocopiable sheets.

Objectives
● To be able to identify a range of local habitats.
● To recognise the importance of protecting habitats.

Resources
Photocopiable page 140 'Habitats'; pens; pencils; coloured pencils; books and pictures for identifying a range of creatures and plants in the local area

Speaking scientifically
habitat, protect

Lesson 3: Protecting habitats

Introduction
It is important for the children to link habitats with the idea that living things need these habitats: without these habitats the creatures and plants that are dependent on them would die. Remind the children where woodlice live. Ask: *What would happen to the woodlice if all the log piles and leaf mould and dark damp places were cleared away?* Talk about where a daisy lives in a field. Ask: *Where would the daisies grow if the field was ploughed up by a farmer?* Remind the children where a frog lives and how its life cycle relies on water for the eggs and tadpoles. Ask: *What would the frogs do if the pond was dried out and a house built on it?*

Whole-class work
1. Ask the children to tell you about all the habitats they have looked at around the school so far. They should be able to suggest flower beds, bushes, the air, dark, wet places, on the grassy field, by the pond and so on.

2. Each time they mention a habitat ask them to tell you what grows there and which creatures use that place as a habitat or, in the case of birds, as part of their habitat.

Group work
3. Give each child photocopiable page 140 'Habitats' and divide them into groups of four or five. They should talk about the work they are doing as a group but complete a photocopiable sheet each. In the 'habitat' column they should write a brief description of the habitat: for example, a wood pile next to the classroom wall, or pond at the corner of the field. Read through the other columns with them and explain that they can just put a tick or a cross, or write something simple such as 'some shade' or 'very wet'. If there are other adults available, children could take their photocopiable sheets outside to complete – but they should know enough about the school grounds to be able to fill in the columns in the classroom.

4. Discuss the completed tables back in the classroom. Ask: *What would happen if we had no shady/dry/sunny/wet areas around the school? What can we do to protect these habitats?*

Differentiation
● Support children who might find completing the photocopiable sheet difficult. They will need reminding of all the work that they have already done to help them to fill in all the columns.
● Challenge children to complete the photocopiable sheet at home using their own garden. They will need to look for a range of habitats and look carefully for a range of plants, animals, insects, birds and so on that live there.

Science in the wider world
Even small-scale habitats support a wide range of living things; as areas become more built up, small-scale habitats are even more important. Local environments are important and need to be protected.

Review
Children can be assessed on how well they complete their photocopiable sheets and answer questions in discussion.

Objectives
● To know about food chains in familiar local habitats.

Resources
Photocopiable page 141 'Food chains'; coloured pencils; rulers

Speaking scientifically
food chain, herbivore, carnivore, omnivore

Lesson 1: Food chains

Introduction

Tell the children that all animals, insects and birds need to eat and that they all eat each other. Ask: *What's a carnivore? What's a herbivore?* Establish that a carnivore eats meat (other animals) and a herbivore eats plants. Some animals eat anything and we are like this. Humans are 'omnivores'.

Talk to the children about a wide range of animals, insects, birds, invertebrates and so on by naming a creature and asking what it eats. Make sure that you include a fox, rabbit, snails and slugs, hedgehogs, sheep, robins and caterpillars.

Whole-class work

1. Use the whiteboard or a flipchart to write some food chains, as follows. Ask the children what a mouse eats – the answer should be seeds. Write 'seeds' on the whiteboard with an arrow pointing to 'mouse'. Ask the children what eats a mouse. They could say hawks or foxes. Draw an arrow from the word 'mouse' to 'fox'. Tell the children that this is a three-stage food chain.

2. Give the whole class another example. Write down the word 'leaf'. Ask them what eats a leaf – probably a caterpillar. Write down 'caterpillar' and an arrow from 'leaf' to 'caterpillar'. Ask them what eats a caterpillar – the answer might be a robin. Write down the word 'robin' with an arrow from 'caterpillar' to 'robin'. This is another example of a three-stage food chain.

3. Ask them where we would be in a three-stage food chain. They should know that most people eat plants and meat. A food chain with us in it could be grass → sheep → human

Group work

4. Give each child photocopiable page 141 'Food chains'. Go through the pictures of different plants and creatures so that the children know what they are. Ask them to colour each of them. Tell the children to use the space underneath to write two, three-stage food chains.

5. Ask them to think of at least one four-stage food chain and a food chain that has humans in it.

6. Give each child a sheet of paper and ask them to choose one of their food chains and to draw and colour each stage, including the arrows to link each of the stages.

Differentiation
● Support children who might find writing the three stages of a food chain difficult. They might need help in deciding what eats what and the correct sequence in the chain.
● Challenge children to produce more four-stage food chains, with different animals.

Science in the wider world

Food chains show how animals depend on each other: if the food chain breaks, some animals will not survive because there won't be enough food for them. This is why it is important to protect all species.

Review

Children can be assessed on how well they can produce food chains, especially those that have four stages.

Objectives
● To understand food chains in less familiar habitats – rainforests.

Resources
Pictures, books or DVDs showing a range of creatures from rainforests; pens; coloured pencils; paints

Speaking scientifically
rainforest, carnivore, herbivore, predator, food chain

Introduction
Remind the children of what a food chain is and ask them for examples of some of the food chains that they know about in the school grounds and the local environment. Write some of their suggestions where they can see them, with the usual arrows joining each stage. For example: leaf → caterpillar → bird; dandelion → rabbit → fox; grass → sheep → human.

Whole-class work
1. Show the class the pictures, books or DVDs of life in the rainforest. Make sure that the books and pictures are easily available for the children to look at. Explain to the children that everything that grows in the rainforest is huge and that there are more reptiles, insects, birds and mammals than where they live. Ask them what they remember about rainforests from previous lessons. They are very wet and very hot and below the canopy it is quite gloomy; many plants and animals live in the canopy where there is more sunlight.

2. Talk to the children about some of the creatures that live in rainforests around the world. There are huge butterflies and other insects, tall trees and creepers; there are frogs, snakes, alligators, crocodiles, apes and monkeys, as well as huge cats such as tigers, jaguars and leopards.

3. Most of the time it seems as if everything is trying to eat everything else. There are many predators and when animals or birds die, and fall onto the forest floor, there are creatures that will eat them there too.

4. Give some examples of rainforest food chains, such as:
flowers → butterfly → spider → bird → ants (when the bird dies);
insects → spiders → bird → snake

Group work
5. Make sure that all the children can see the examples of rainforest food chains and have access to a range of secondary sources. Ask them to draw their own food chain on a piece of paper and label it with arrows from stage to stage. Tell them to work in small groups of no more than four. They must choose a food chain and draw the creatures in it. Once they have coloured or painted their creatures they can cut them out.

6. One way of displaying their food chains is to mount them on display boards; or they could be mounted on string and hung in the classroom in some way.

Differentiation
● Some children will need support in using the secondary sources to find food chains of their own.
● Challenge children to draw more than one food chain. Give them starting points, for example a spider, an ant, or fruit, and ask them to make a food chain with at least four stages.

Science in the wider world
Rainforests are home to many, many plants and a wide range of different creatures. Children need to know as much about them as possible so that they can take decisions about how they can be preserved.

Review
Children can be assessed on how well they can create four-stage food chains and how successfully they use secondary sources.

Objectives
● To understand food chains in less familiar habitats – oceans.

Resources
Pictures, books and DVDs showing a wide range of creatures living in the oceans; coloured pencils; paint; scissors; glue; masking tape or similar

Speaking scientifically
plankton, predator

Lesson 3: Ocean food chains

Introduction
Talk to the children about some of the creatures that they found when they studied their local pond. Ask them if they can think of some simple food chains that involve creatures that live in or around the water. An example might include:
flower → insect → frog

Whole-class work
1. Oceans are enormous areas of salt water. Use the pictures, books and DVDs to find out the names of ocean creatures. This shouldn't take too long because the children will have looked at some sea creatures before. These names could be written where the children can see them. Make sure that tiny creatures such as plankton and shrimps are included, as well as small fish such as mackerel, and larger predators, such as sharks, squid, whales, seals and penguins.

2. Ask: *What kind of animal are seals and whales?* Tell the children that they are mammals. Talk about penguins being birds that can't fly.

3. Remind the children that, like rainforests, the oceans depend on the sun for light and warmth and that almost all ocean food chains start with tiny creatures called plankton. Ask them if they can think of any food chains. There is a very simple one: plankton → whales.

Other food chains might include:
plankton → shrimps → mackerel → penguin
plankton → shrimps → mackerel → seal → shark

Group work
4. Ask each child to draw and label their own ocean food chain. They will need to be able to see the pictures and books. Make sure that there are lots of photographs of different kinds of plankton.

5. Arrange the children in groups of four and ask each group to choose one of their ocean food chains. They will need to draw each stage in the chain large enough to be cut out.

6. When each of the drawings have been cut out, place a long piece of masking tape on the table and stick each stage of the food chain onto it with the plankton stage at the bottom and the final stage – the large predator – at the top. These can be hung in the classroom to show a variety of ocean food chains.

> ### Differentiation
> ● Support children who have difficulty drawing and labelling their own food chains.
> ● Challenge children to find out more about plankton and other microscopic creatures, such as krill. What do they think would happen to life in the oceans if there was less plankton?

Science in the wider world
All life in the ocean is dependent on there being lots of plankton. It is essential: if there was less plankton there would be less of everything else, including the fish that we eat.

Review
The children can be assessed on how well they complete their individual food chains and use secondary sources.

■SCHOLASTIC

Objectives
● To understand that living creatures move through their habitats in different ways.
● To know that creatures are able to adapt to the different habitats that they live in.

Resources
Spades; small containers; access to a flower bed or somewhere to look for earthworms; paper towels; magnifying lenses; coloured pencils; access to school grounds

Speaking scientifically
earthworm, movement, habitat

Lesson 1: Adapting to habitats

Introduction
Remind the children that specific creatures live in specific habitats. Ask: *How does a bird manage to live in the air?* They should tell you that birds have wings and can fly. Ask: *How do woodlice survive in dark, damp conditions?* They live on rotting wood and leaves. *Why do rabbits live on the edges of woods and fields?* They need to eat grass and leaves and so live underground in holes at the edges of fields or in woods. Ask: *How are fish suited to living in water?* They breathe underwater and can move through the water smoothly and easily.

Whole-class work
1. Tell the children that they are going to look at one creature that lives very close to the school in a very specific habitat – an earthworm – and they are going to find out how it moves. Ask: *Where do worms live?* The children should know that worms are found in the ground because they get all the food they need from the soil.

2. Take the children outside and find an area of loose earth to dig for worms. It is better to do this on a damp day, or to water the soil well to bring the worms closer to the surface before you dig.

3. When they have collected enough large, whole worms – one between four children – put them into the containers and take them back to the classroom.

Group work
4. Each group needs to dampen a paper towel. The worm should be able to move around on it. When the worm has been carefully placed on the paper towel tell the children to watch it move. Ask: *What shape is the head end? What shape is the tail end?*

5. Tell the children to put their ear close to the moving earthworm. Ask: *What can you hear?* The earthworm has bristles and should scrape as it moves.

6. Tell the children to turn the earthworm over and gently rub a finger along the skin. Ask: *What can you feel?*

Individual work
7. Tell the children to look at the earthworm with a magnifying lens and draw a detailed picture of what they can see.

8. Ask them to write down a description of how the worm moves and say why they think it finds it easy to live and move around in its environment.

> ### Differentiation
> ● Support children who will need help in touching the earthworm and who might also find it difficult to describe how it moves.
> ● Challenge children to find out about an earthworm's life cycle and why gardeners think earthworms are wonderful and helpful creatures.

Science in the wider world
Earthworms are very useful in breaking down soil. They help to create better soil for growing the crops that we eat.

Review
Children can be assessed on how well they draw the closely observed worm and how well they describe how it moves.

Resources
Photocopiable page 142 'Planning a wildlife area'; scissors; glue

Speaking scientifically
habitat, wildlife, planning, tree nursery

Lesson 2: Designing habitats

Introduction
Tell the children that during the next two lessons they will be planning wildlife areas that have a wide variety of different habitats. Begin by telling the children the names of a range of creatures and plants in the school grounds, such as woodlouse, daisy, clover, blackbird, frog, stickleback, earthworm, robin, holly bush, daffodil, spider, moss and trees. As soon as you say the name, they should immediately tell you the habitat that this creature or plant needs.

Whole-class work
1. This activity is the opposite of the introduction. This time you will name a variety of different habitats and give the children one or two minutes to talk to their neighbours and then tell you the different creatures that live in this habitat. They should find this easy because they have looked at different habitats before and they have also explored which creatures and which plants live in various habitats.

2. Start off with a pond. They should be able to list fish, dragonflies, frogs and so on.

3. Try a log pile next. They should suggest things like slugs, woodlice and spiders.

4. What about the field as a habitat? They should mention clover and daisies as well as birds that need insects and worms under the ground.

5. Discuss all the habitats that are in the school grounds or that the children have explored in the local environment.

Group work
6. Give each child photocopiable page 142 'Planning a wildlife area' and explain that they are going to create a wildlife area that has a range of different habitats. Before they start work on the photocopiable sheet, talk about what a tree nursery is and why we need butterfly gardens and wildlife meadows. Ask: *What will be special about the butterfly garden?* Explain that it will have flowers that are attractive to butterflies and other insects.

7. First of all ask them to colour in each of the small pictures. When they have done this, they need to talk to other children at the table and decide where to glue their pictures on the plan. Make sure they consider which items need shade, which need sunshine, which need open spaces and which need shelter from the wind.

> **Differentiation**
> ● Support children who need help in deciding where to put the different habitats on their plan.
> ● Challenge children to tell you which animals and plants will be attracted to their wildlife area. What will they eat and where will they find shelter?

Science in the wider world
Preserving habitats such as rainforests and oceans is a world issue, but we can all preserve habitats closer to home and, more importantly, we can all help to create new wildlife areas with new habitats.

Review
Children could be assessed on how creative they are in planning their wildlife area, and how well they understand how to create a range of habitats.

Objectives
● To begin to understand how habitats can be created and preserved.

Resources
Completed photocopiable page 142 'Planning a wildlife area; a simple plan of the school (A4 size) for each child; a large plan of the school mounted on a display board; pencils; coloured pencils

Speaking scientifically
habitat, wildlife, planning

Lesson 3: Improving habitats

Introduction
Each child needs their own completed photocopiable page 142 'Planning a wildlife area' sheet from the previous lesson. Ask for two or three volunteers to explain how they have planned their wildlife area to the rest of the class.

Make sure that during these short explanations the whole class is aware of the importance of different habitats. They also need to understand the range of creatures and plants that live in them.

Whole-class work
1. Ask the children to tell you all the habitats they have found in the school grounds and the creatures and plants that live there. Don't spend too much time on this because it has been explored before.

2. Tell them that they are going to design a school wildlife area – or redesign the existing one. It is possible to do this even if you have only a small, urban space.

3. Talk about any wildlife habitats you have already, where they are and how they could be improved. For example: there might be a small space for rotting logs and other vegetation and you might want to make it bigger; the field might be big enough to have a small area left uncut for a wildflower meadow; the bushes and hedges might be ornamental shrubs and it might be possible to make a new hedge using native British bushes; if there isn't a pond, perhaps one could one be made.

Group work
4. Give each child a copy of the A4-sized plan of the school. Ask them to work in groups of four or five but to complete a sheet each.

5. Quickly go through the range of habitats on their photocopiable sheet and tell them that they have to decide where they want each area to go on the school plan. If some of these areas already exist they could stay in exactly the same place, or they could be moved somewhere else if appropriate.

6. Tell the children to discuss where each area will go with their group and then draw the area in the right place on their own plan of the school.

7. When they have finished, choose different groups of children to draw a habitat each on the large plan of the school on display.

8. Invite other classes to look at your ideas. Discuss whether they would work. Would creating these habitats attract more creatures and allow a wider range of plants to grow?

Differentiation
● Support children who have difficulty placing different habitats on their school plans.
● Challenge children to label each of the habitats on the large display board with the creatures and plants that might live there.

Review
The children can be assessed on how well they can record data on their own plan of the school, and on their understanding of how habitats can be created.

Objectives
● To assess whether the children understand that there are several different habitats in and around the school and the local environment.
● To assess whether the children understand that there is a wide range of different plants and animals living in each habitat.

Resources
Access to the school grounds or other local environments visited previously

Working scientifically
● Using their observations and ideas to suggest answers to questions.
● Use simple secondary sources to find answers.

Different habitats and different creatures

Revise

● It is important to look carefully, for the last time, at local wildlife habitats. The children will have used the school grounds or another local environment to study what the habitats look like, as well as the kind of creatures and plants that grow there.

● This revision will work best if the children walk round all the areas that they have been studying so that they see each habitat again. As you take them out ask them a range of questions about each habitat. For example: *What does the log pile look like? Is it dry and cold or warm and damp underneath? Is it dark or light? How is the pond different from the meadow? How are the bushes and shrubs different from the trees? How are any rocks and gravel areas different from the edges of the pond?* This last example will make the children think about damp and dry.

● During the walk around the school grounds or local environment take advantage of any creatures that you see. If the children see a bird, ask them what habitats it needs to live, eat and reproduce. Talk to them about some common creatures that will use the grounds but that they probably will never see. These are creatures that either hide themselves well or come out at night. For example, ask: *What habitat does a squirrel need? What food will a fox eat and where will it get it from? What does a hedgehog need to eat? Where will it find it?*

● Plants are also important and need certain habitats. Common ones, such as a daisy, clover and dandelion, need open grass or wasteland. Ask the children what they think pond plants need. *Are there many plants growing in dark, shady places? If not, why not?*

Assess

● Give the children pieces of paper and ask them to complete theses questions and statements:
  ● Draw a log pile and write down the names of three creatures that might live there.
  ● Write down the names of two creatures that use trees as their habitat.
  ● Why does a blackbird need a habitat with bushes and grass?
  ● Where would you find a frog?
  ● A spider likes to live in _____.
  ● A dandelion likes to grow in _____.
  ● Woodlice live in _____.
  ● Butterflies get their food from _____.
  ● Two creatures that eat seeds are _____ and _____.

Further practice

● The whole point of this assess and review lesson is to link specific creatures to specific habitats. The children should be able to respond accurately to the first four questions. Some of the statements could be more difficult and the children could be allowed to use secondary sources to find the answers.

● Other questions they could research are: *What kind of creature is a woodlouse? Is a spider an insect? If not, what is it? What kind of habitat do squirrels need?*

Objectives
● To assess whether the children understand the range of living things that live in deserts, rainforests, seas and rivers.

Resources
Pictures and books on deserts, rainforests and oceans; a globe; paper (several sheets each); coloured pencils; scissors and glue; interactive activity 'Different habitats' on the CD-ROM

Working scientifically
● Use secondary sources to find answers.

Deserts and rainforests, rivers and seas

Revise
● Deserts and rainforests, rivers and seas are very different from where the children live and the kinds of ponds or rivers that they might have seen. It is important to help them to understand these differences.
● Use pictures and books to explore the dry, sandy and rocky conditions in a desert. Compare some of the desert temperatures with the ones that we experience in summer. Look at some of the desert animals, especially snakes and lizards, and plants such as cacti. Ask the children how cacti can survive without water. Find out where the creatures actually live: many have burrows under the sand and rocks.
● Remind the children that rainforests are dark, damp and very wet. Try to help them to understand how big the trees are and how dense the creepers and plants are that hang off the trees. Look at some of the animals that live in rainforests. Many live in the tops of the trees (the canopy), such as apes, monkeys and birds. Discuss what most of the monkeys eat: explain that because the plants are so large and grow so easily there is always a supply of leaves and fruit.
● Complete the first screen of interactive activity 'Different habitats' on the CD-ROM as a class.
● Seas and rivers cover a large part of the earth's surface. Show the children a globe and leave it in the classroom together with a large map of the world. Tell them the names of the oceans and let them appreciate how much water there actually is.
● Talks about the kinds of fish, and mammals such as otters and water voles that live in the rivers near where they live. In rivers in other countries there are alligators and crocodiles and large mammals such as water buffalo and hippopotamus.
● Talk about the huge whales and sharks that live in the sea and birds such as the albatross, which can fly thousands of miles. Don't forget to remind the children that mammals such as whales, seals and dolphins live in the sea, and that birds such as penguins rely on the sea for their food. There are also strange creatures, such as giant squid and huge jellyfish.
● Complete the second screen of interactive activity 'Different habitats' on the CD-ROM as a class.

Assess
● Give each child three pieces of paper and ask them to write one title on each sheet, as follows: 'Deserts', 'Rainforests', 'Oceans'.
● Tell them that they can use the books and pictures to help them to draw and colour a desert, a rainforest and an ocean.
● Remove all the books and pictures and provide some more paper.
● Tell the children to draw, colour in and then cut out and stick onto the appropriate sheet, the following: one desert plant and three desert creatures; one rainforest plant and three rainforest creatures; one ocean plant and three ocean creatures.

Further practice
● If the children are really interested in any of the three habitats in this lesson, they could look closely at specific creatures. For example, there are strange and wonderful frogs in the rainforests – some of them are venemous and can kill. There are spiders that hide in holes and scorpions with stings on their tails in the deserts; and in the depths of the oceans are fish with lights on their heads.

● To assess whether the children understand food chains in local habitats and in less familiar habitats.

Resources
Pictures and books of a wide range of creatures and plants that live: locally, in deserts, in rainforests, and in oceans; pencils; paper (four sheets each)

Working scientifically
● Using their observations to answer questions.

Food chains

Revise

● Instead of just looking at and recognising the range of animals that live in different habitats, the children need to understand what each creature eats and how they are linked together in food chains.

● Start by looking at creatures in local habitats. Show the children pictures and ask the simple question: *What does this creature eat?* They should know the answers because they have explored carnivores, herbivores and omnivores before. They might need reminding what a predator is.

● Ask: *What do butterflies/birds eat? What do rabbits/foxes/frogs eat? What about sheep – what kind of habitat do they need? What about us – what do we eat that you might find in the local environment?* Answers to this last question could include plants, such as wheat in a wheat field, but the children need to remember that we are omnivores and eat meat and plants, so we might choose to eat sheep and ducks.

● Suggest a few simple food chains such as: plant → rabbit → fox.

● Show the children some pictures of desert creatures. Food chains begin to get more complicated because there are fewer plant eaters and most creatures are predators. Most of the insects will eat each other and the lizards and snakes will eat the insects. There will be some mammals such as coyotes. Show the children a simple desert food chain.

● Rainforests also have a wide range of predators, but because the forest floor is so dark and damp all the creatures – even large ones – that fall on it are also eaten by ants and other insects. Talk about birds eating fruit and then being eaten by snakes or carnivorous cats, such as jaguars and leopards. Small monkeys will also eat fruit and then be eaten by snakes or leopards. Show the children a simple rainforest food chain.

● Oceans are similar to deserts and rainforests because all the creatures that live there prey on each other. Remind the children that life in the oceans is dependent on plankton and other tiny creatures. Even some huge whales – the largest creatures on earth – live entirely on plankton. Most of the food chains in the ocean start with small creatures that get eaten by larger fish, which then get eaten by even larger fish or squid. Remind the children that there is another chain that has mammals and birds in it. Show the children a simple food chain using penguins or seals.

Assess

● Give the children four sheets of paper and ask hem to write these headings on separate sheets: 'Local food chains', 'Desert food chains', 'Rainforest food chains' and 'Ocean food chains'.

● Tell them to use each piece of paper in turn and to draw and label a food chain on each one. Show them how to do it by drawing and labelling a simple food chain on the whiteboard. Leave this example where the children can see it.

● Explain that the best ones will be the most detailed chains with at least three stages. Remind them to draw each stage with an arrow.

Further practice

● Most children will understand exactly what food chains are but might not realise that humans are at the top – or at the end – of lots of chains. Tell the children to write down some of the food chains where they are one of the stages.

Habitats in the school grounds

■ Draw these different habitats – in the left-hand box.
■ Draw some of the creatures that live in each habitat in the right-hand box.

In the air	
Trees and bushes	
Grass and flowers	
Under stones	
Rotting wood	

I can draw different habitats.

How did you do?

Minibeast sampling

■ Compare the minibeasts found in three different areas: a rocky place (A), a grassy place (B) and a dark, damp place (C).

■ Complete the table below.

Area	Number of minibeasts found	Names of minibeasts found	Drawing of one minibeast
rocky place			
grassy place			
dark, damp place			

I can complete a table with my observations.

How did you do?

Birds' beaks

- Colour in the birds.
- Draw lines to join each food to the correct type of beak.

water plants

small mammals or other birds

nuts and seeds

insects

I can match items correctly.

How did you do?

Where plants live

■ Draw lines to match each plant with its habitat.

moss

oak tree

daisy

tulip

mushroom

thistle

flower bed

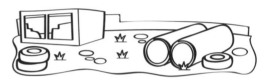

waste ground

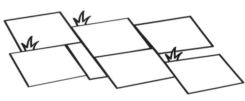

paving stones

rotten log

lawn

I can match plants to their habitats correctly.

How did you do?

137

PHOTOCOPIABLE

Pond life

■ Draw lines to match each creature with its habitat.

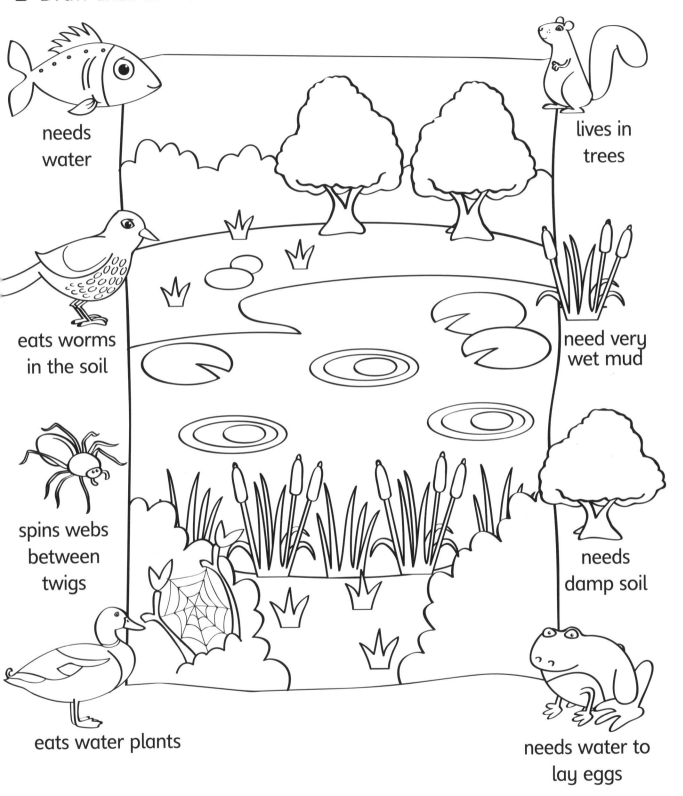

needs
water

lives in
trees

eats worms
in the soil

need very
wet mud

spins webs
between
twigs

needs
damp soil

eats water plants

needs water to
lay eggs

I can match creatures to their habitats correctly.

How did you do?

Name: _____

Date: _____

Habitats

■ Complete the table below for habitats around the school.

Habitat	wet	dry	sunny	shady	plants	animals
1.						
2.						
3.						
4.						

I can complete a table with my observations.

PHOTOCOPIABLE

SCHOLASTIC
www.scholastic.co.uk

Food chains

■ Look at the pictures below and create some food chains.
■ One example has been done for you.

_____ grass _____ → _____ mouse _____ → _____ tawny owl _____

_____ → _____ → _____

_____ → _____ → _____

_____ → _____ → _____ → _____

_____ → _____ → _____ → _____

_____

I can create food chains.

How did you do?

Planning a wildlife area

■ Willow Field Primary School is planning a wildlife area.

■ Cut out the pictures from the bottom of the page and stick each one onto the plan of the school below, in the place that you think is best.

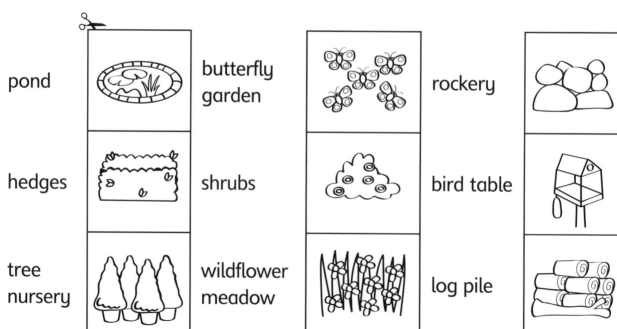

pond

butterfly garden

rockery

hedges

shrubs

bird table

tree nursery

wildflower meadow

log pile

Uses of everyday materials

Expected prior learning
- The names of common materials, such as wood, metal, plastic.
- Some of the uses of common materials, such as wooden chairs, metal cutlery and so on.
- To be able to recognise materials in everyday situations, such as school and home.
- To be able to recognise that some objects, such as a table, have been made – they have been manufactured from common materials.

Overview of progression
After completing this chapter they should know:
- how to identify a variety of everyday materials
- how to compare everyday materials in the home and at school
- that some common objects can be made of different materials
- that metals and wood are used to make lots of different objects
- that some materials are natural and some are manufactured.

Creative context
- This chapter provides opportunities to look closely at and draw a range of objects, such as a bicycle and various toys, and to use different visual images to illustrate their findings. They will need to use their skills in design and food technology to make cakes and ice lollies.

Background knowledge
Materials in common objects
- Different materials are often used to make the same things, for example, spoons. Many common objects are made from a variety of materials, each of which is used because of its specific properties. For example, school chairs are made of plastic and metal because the plastic is light and durable and easy to clean. The legs are made of metal to add strength.

Using materials
- Certain materials are useful. There are differences between natural materials and those that are manufactured. When we mix, heat or freeze certain materials they can change state.

Speaking scientifically
- The children should know the names of a wide range of materials, including wood, metal, plastic, rubber, water, rock, soil and so on.
- They should also understand what mixing, heating and freezing mean.

Preparation
You will need to provide: samples and pictures of objects made of wood, glass, metal, plastic, stone, rubber, wool, cotton, paper, polythene; the following objects, each made from a variety of materials – floor coverings, chairs, tables, chopping boards, plates, spoons, toys, threads, clothes (with manufacturers' labels); coins from different countries; pieces of bark; sections of logs; photos of a cotton plant, flax plant and sheep; an adult's bicycle; hats, gloves, boots and scarves; photos of clothing for extreme cold and hot weather; magnifying lenses; clear plastic bottles; stirring rods; pictures of wasp, bumble bee, hamster, mouse and birds' nests; real examples of a disused wasp or birds' nest; small glass jars with lids; insulating materials; thermometers; warm water; coal; sand; silk; natural sponge; cake-making equipment and ingredients (see recipe on CD-ROM); access to an oven; ice-cube trays; ice-lolly moulds; fruit juices; pictures of complex common objects such as vehicles or a vacuum cleaner; adult volunteers

On the CD-ROM you will find: photocopiable pages 'Cake recipe', 'Comparing materials', 'The life cycle of a bird'; interactive activities 'What's it made from?', 'Clothes'

Chapter at a glance

Week	Lesson	Curriculum objectives	Objectives	Main activity	Working scientifically
1	1	• To revise the objectives of Year 1. • To identify and name a variety of everyday materials.	• To revise the names of common materials. • To introduce the idea that there are many different uses for materials.	Discussing a range of materials from practical examples and secondary sources. Looking at a selection of materials and discussing their uses.	• Identifying and classifying. • Gathering and recording data.
	2	• To identify and name a variety of everyday materials.	• To understand that there are many different materials.	Classroom survey of the range of materials they can see and what they are used for. Group charts matching materials to objects. Labelling a picture of a classroom.	• Observing closely. • Gathering and recording data.
	3	• To identify and name a variety of everyday materials.	• To understand that there are many different materials.	School building and grounds survey of the range of materials they can see and what they are used for. Group charts matching materials to objects. Painting a picture of the local area.	• Observing closely. • Gathering and recording data.
2	1	• To identify and compare the suitability of a variety of everyday materials for particular uses.	• To understand and recognise the wide range of different materials that we need at home.	Discussing what they have in their kitchens at home. Using a kitchen diagram to label materials.	• Observing closely. • Gathering and recording data.
	2	• To identify and compare the suitability of a variety of everyday materials for particular uses.	• To understand that different materials can be used to make the same things.	Discussing objects that can be made from more than one type of material and recognising what they can be made from. Completing diagrams and sentences.	• Using their observations to suggest answers to questions.
	3	• Identify and discuss the uses of different everyday materials.	• To understand that spoons made of different materials have different uses.	Discussing the different materials used to make spoons. Completing a spoon chart.	• Using their observations to suggest answers to questions.
3	1	• Identify and discuss the uses of different everyday materials.	• To know that clothes are made from lots of different materials.	Comparing and discussing different types of toy – what they are made from and why. Completing a toy diagram.	• Using their observations to suggest answers to questions.
	2	• Identify and discuss the uses of different everyday materials.	• To know that toys are made from lots of different materials.	Comparing and discussing different types of clothes – what they are made from and why. Completing a clothes diagram.	• Using their observations to suggest answers to questions.
	3	• Identify and discuss the uses of different everyday materials.	• To know that a bicycle is made from lots of different materials.	Looking closely at a bicycle and finding out what materials have been used to make it. Completing a bicycle diagram and sentences.	• Using their observations to suggest answers to questions.

Chapter at a glance

Week	Lesson	Curriculum objectives	Objectives	Main activity	Working scientifically
4	1	• Identify and discuss the uses of different everyday materials.	• To know that some materials are used to help us to keep warm.	Discussing how we keep warm and the clothes we wear that help us. Completing sentences and labelling drawings.	• Using their observations to suggest answers to questions.
	2	• Identify and discuss the uses of different everyday materials.	• To know that metals are used for many things.	Discussing what metals are and the uses for metals – coins, cans, cars, etc. Drawing objects made from metal. Coin and brass rubbing.	• Using their observations to suggest answers to questions.
	3	• Identify and discuss the uses of different everyday materials.	• To know that wood has many uses. • To know that wood comes from trees and that woods from different types of tree are not the same.	Discussing what wood is and its different uses. Bark rubbings. Completing a photocopiable page.	• Using their observations to suggest answers to questions.
5	1	• Identify and discuss the uses of different everyday materials.	• To understand what soil is and what it is useful for.	Researching the question – What is soil and how is it useful? Group investigation identifying and recording different materials in soil.	• Using their observations to suggest answers to questions. • Performing simple tests. • Gathering and recording data.
	2	• Identify and discuss the uses of different everyday materials.	• To know that mammals, birds and insects use materials. • To find out which materials are good insulators.	Discussing the materials used in different nests. Group investigation into different insulating materials.	• Using their observations to suggest answers to questions. • Performing simple tests. • Gathering and recording data.
	3	• Identify and discuss the uses of different everyday materials.	• To understand why different materials are used for different things.	Discussing objects and why they are made from certain materials. Drawing rooms and objects made from inappropriate materials, in 'Strange Land'.	• Using their observations and ideas to suggest answers to questions.
6	1	• Identify and discuss the uses of different everyday materials.	• To understand that some materials are natural and others have to be manufactured.	Classifying different materials as 'natural' or 'manufactured'.	• Identifying and classifying.
	2	• Identify and discuss the uses of different everyday materials.	• To know the different materials needed to make a cake. • To know that the materials need to be mixed and heated and placed in a container to make a cake.	Looking at and identifying materials needed to make a cake and where they come from. Making a cake and recording what they do and what happens.	• Using their observations to suggest answers to questions.
	3	• Identify and discuss the uses of different everyday materials.	• To understand that if we freeze some materials they change into something else.	Discussing the differences between water and ice. Freezing fruit juices and recording what happens.	• Using their observations to suggest answers to questions.
Assess and review					

Objectives
● To revise the names of common materials.
● To introduce the idea that there are many different uses for materials.

Resources
Samples of materials (including wood, glass, metal, plastic, stone, rubber, materials such as wool and cotton, paper, polythene bags); pictures of a range of materials; photocopiable page 168 'Describing materials'

Speaking scientifically
shiny, dull, bendy, stiff, waterproof, absorb, material, uses

Lesson 1: Everyday materials

Previous knowledge
Many of the materials will be known by the children from their everyday experiences, but this lesson introduces the children to the idea that there are many different materials and that they have many different uses.

Introduction
Ensure that all children have a pencil on their table. Remind them that what they are wearing, what they are sitting on and all the objects in the classroom are made from different materials. Make sure that they know that 'materials' does not just mean fabric like wool and cotton but can mean lots of other things. For example, ask them to pick up their pencils and ask them what materials it is made from. They should know wood and they might also know that the central core is graphite. Ask them what material they write on: they will all know that they write on paper.

Whole-class work
1. Show the children all the different materials that you have collected. Do this slowly, one at a time, and ask the children to tell you what the material is and then to describe it. Encourage them to use words such as: soft, hard, shiny, bendy, stiff, dull, cold, warm, heavy and so on. Make sure that they can name wood, plastic, metal, rubber and glass.

2. They should also know where wood comes from. If you can get hold of different kinds of wood, such as oak, beech and pine, they will notice the different grains in the wood and see that they are very different.

3. Ask: *Where do you think metal comes from?* Tell them that it starts as ore (for example, iron ore), which is a mineral found in the ground.

4. Ask: *What about rubber?* Explain to them that rubber is a sap that is collected from certain trees.

Individual work
5. Ask the children to draw a detailed, coloured picture of a car.

6. When all the children have drawn their car discuss what materials it is made from. They should know that there is glass in the windows, plastic on the dashboard and the inside of the doors, fabric for the seats, rubber for the tyres and metal for the body. Write the names of the materials where they can see them. They should then write the words around their picture and draw lines from each material to the appropriate part of the car.

Group work
7. There are two different group activities for the children: completing the photocopiable sheet and creating a list of materials and their uses. They can discuss their work as a group, but each child should complete their own photocopiable sheet. The children need to be able to touch and feel the materials that you have shown them and that they have named and tried to describe.

8. Give each child photocopiable page 168 'Describing materials'. Read through the names of the materials at the top of the photocopiable sheet. Show them your examples of the same materials and make sure they can move around the room and touch them. Explain that they need to draw a picture of each material in the correct sorting ring. There will be more than one picture in each ring and some materials might appear in several rings. Use wood as an example and ask them where they would draw a simple picture of a piece of wood. They should realise that it should go in the rings for dull, hard and stiff. You may want to increase the size of the photocopiable sheets to A3.

9. When they have finished ask them questions about where they have drawn their pictures. For example: *Which materials do you think soak up water? Which material soaks up water when you have a bath?* Talk about real sponges being natural, living things that come from the sea. Ask: *Which materials do you think are waterproof?* They should have included polythene and plastic but could also have included metal.

10. Ask them to look at each of the materials at the top of the sheet. Allow them to talk to other children on their table and ask them to think about this question: *What is each of the materials used for?* (Tell them just to think of paper when they get to the paper towel.) Talk about each of the materials in turn. They should be able to give you a wide range of things they think are made of wood, cotton, paper and metal; but rubber, plastic and polythene may be more difficult.

11. Give each child another piece of paper. Tell them to place it on their table portrait way up and divide it into three columns. The columns should be headed 'Material', 'Description' and 'Uses'. Write down these materials on the whiteboard: wood, metal, plastic, paper. Tell them to write down each material in turn in the left-hand column and write a description of the material in the middle column. In the right-hand column they should write down as many ways of using this material as they can think of. If there is space they could draw one of the ways of using each material.

Introducing the new area of study

Read or tell the story of 'The three little pigs'. Discuss which pig was the most sensible and the different materials they used. Ask the children why they think the brick house was the strongest. Can they think of anything else that can be used to build a house? Explain that they will be learning about different materials and how they are used – not just in houses, but in toys, clothes, jewellery, machinery and many other things.

> **Differentiation**
> ● Parts of this lesson will be difficult for some children. Support them when they are completing the photocopiable sheet and when they are trying to describe different materials.
> ● Challenge children to list as many uses for different materials as possible. They could also be shown some rock and sand. Ask them to describe these materials in detail and then ask them to find out what they are used for.

Science in the wider world

We are surrounded by different materials and would not be able to sustain how we live without them. It is important for children to know what they are, where we get them from and how they are manufactured into things that we use.

Review

Children can be assessed on how well they describe different materials and how many different uses they find for each of them.

Objectives
● To understand that there are many different materials.

Resources
Samples of plastic, metal, wood, fabric, paper, rubber and glass; photocopiable page 169 'In the classroom'; clipboards; coloured pencils; glue; scissors

Speaking scientifically
plastic, wood, fabric, paper, rubber, glass, metal

Lesson 2: Everyday materials in the classroom

Introduction
Show the class a selection of different materials again to remind them exactly what they look like. Make sure that the materials include: plastic, wood, fabric, paper, rubber and glass. Ask questions such as: *Is it shiny? Is it hard? Do you think it is waterproof? Could you bend this material?*

Whole-class work
1. Make sure that the materials are available for the children to look at and touch. Give each child a piece of paper and ask them write the following materials as headings along the top: plastic, metal, wood, fabric, paper, rubber, glass. Tell the children to write down materials that they can observe and touch without moving from their seats. For example, if they can touch their wooden pencils they need to write 'pencils' under 'wood' on their paper; if their desks or tables have metal legs, they should write down 'table' under 'metal' on their paper. Allow about five minutes for this and then ask them to tell you some of the materials that they can touch. Make a list where the children can see it.

Individual work
2. Use the same list of materials and tell the children to attach their paper to their clipboard and walk around the classroom listing all the materials they can find. This time it should include things such as glass in the windows, plastic in the glue bottles and so on. After five minutes ask them to tell you what they have found. Write a list where they can see it.

3. Provide each child with a clean sheet of paper and ask them to draw an object that they found in the classroom. Organise this in such a way that there is a variety of materials. The drawings could be cut out and mounted on a display board that has been divided into columns headed 'plastic', 'wood', 'metal' and so on.

4. Finally, give each child photocopiable page 169 'In the classroom' and ask them label the different materials and colour it in.

Differentiation
● Some children will need support in writing down what they see and in identifying what each object is made of.
● Challenge some children to look more closely at some objects and break them down into all the different materials. For example, a table might have wooden legs and a plastic top. When they are drawing their object they could label it with all the different materials.

Science in the wider world
It is important for children to realise how dependent we are on a wide range of materials. To help them to recognise this dependency ask: *What would we do if we hadn't got the metal table with the wood and plastic top?*

Review
Children can be assessed on how well they complete the photocopiable sheet and how well they can identify a range of materials in the classroom.

Objectives
● To understand that there are many different materials.

Resources
Clipboards; small pieces of paper; adult volunteers to help take the children for a walk around the local neighbourhood; large art paper; pencils; coloured pencils; paints; thread

Speaking scientifically
materials, brick, stone, concrete, slate, metal, plastic, glass, wood, fabric

Lesson 3: Everyday materials in the school

Introduction
Talk about the materials that the children found in their classroom in the previous lesson. Go through each of these materials and for each one ask the class to remind you what they found that was made of this material. They should be able to provide you with a list of almost everything in the classroom.

Tell them how important these materials are. Ask: *What would happen if there was nothing in the classroom made of wood or metal? What would the world be like without glass? What could we use instead? What if we hadn't got any paper?*

Whole-class work
I. Give out the clipboards and one or two sheets of paper for each child and tell them that they are going to walk around the local area and make observations about the different materials that have been used. During the walk stop frequently to allow the children to write down what they can see and draw quick, labelled sketches. Point out some materials that they might not notice, such as the paving slabs they are walking on. Tell them about bricks and slates in houses, and metal in postboxes. If there are some ornate buildings, or shop fronts that have a variety of materials, talk about all these.

2. When the children return to the classroom ask them to explain what they have seen. Ask specific questions, such as: *What materials were the shops made of? What were the houses made of?*

Group work
3. Divide the children into groups of four and give each group a large piece of art paper, pencils and paints. Explain that each group should draw and paint part of where they went on the walk. Allocate a part of the walk to each group; don't allow any choice or there won't be enough variety.

4. These large paintings can form part of a montage of the local environment. Display them around the classroom and write all the appropriate labels of different materials, such as brick, stone, glass, wood, plastic, metal and so on. Join all these labels to the appropriate parts of the pictures with lengths of thread.

Differentiation
● Support some children during the walk and help them to identify and write down the materials that they see in the streets and in the actual buildings.
● Challenge some children to look carefully and closely at the details of the materials that they see. For example, the front doors of houses and shops will contain several materials. Ask them to draw some of the details with clear labels.

Science in the wider world
The range and quantity of materials that we use every day will become clear to the children. We are dependent on more and more different materials and the more people there are, the more materials will be required.

Review
The children can be assessed on how many materials they identify during the walk.

Objectives
● To understand and recognise the wide range of different materials that we need at home.

Resources
Photocopiable page 170 'In the kitchen'; a selection of kitchen implements that the children have been asked to bring to school from home (this will have to be pre-planned – no sharp items!); coloured pencils; scissors; glue

Speaking scientifically
materials, metal, wood, glass, plastic, textiles, china, pottery

Lesson 1: Everyday materials at home

Introduction
Ask the children to quickly name two things they can see in the classroom that are made of paper and three or four that are made of wood or metal. Which objects can they see that are plastic or glass? Are there any objects in the classroom that are made of china or pottery?

Whole-class work
1. Make sure that each child has their object that they have brought to school from their kitchen at home. (It would be a good idea to have a few spares that you have brought into school for children who haven't brought anything – this lesson won't work very well unless everyone has something.) Talk about some of the objects. Ask the children what they are made of. *Are any just made of one material? Are there any made of two or even three materials?*

2. Say to the whole class: *Hold up your kitchen object if it is mainly wood. Hold it up if it is mainly plastic. Hold up your object if it is mainly metal. Does anyone have an object that is made of metal and plastic? Hold it up. Hold up your object if it is made of china or pottery.*

Group work
3. Ask each child to draw the object they have brought from their kitchen (or a spare that you have given to them) and then cut it out. These drawings can be labelled with the correct materials and mounted as a display.

4. Give each child photocopiable page 170 'In the kitchen' and explain to them how to complete it.

5. When they have finished ask them questions about the photocopiable sheet: *What are the names of the metal objects? How many objects are made from textiles? What are they? Tell me the names of some of the plastic objects. What objects do you think might have been made of metal and plastic? Are there any wooden objects? What are they?*

Differentiation
● Some children will need support in completing the photocopiable sheet. They may not know the names of some of the objects.
● Challenge children to think about their own bedrooms or living rooms and to write down a list of objects, and alongside each one write down what it is made from. Televisions and computers are complex: the children should look at books that might break them down into different materials.

Science in the wider world
Once again, this lesson is about the range of materials that we are dependent on.

Review
The children could be assessed on how well they complete the photocopiable sheet.

Objectives
● To understand that different materials can be used to make the same things.

Resources
A range of objects made from different materials (floor covering – carpet, plastic, wood; chairs – wooden, plastic, fabric; chopping boards – plastic, wooden, glass; plates – paper, glass, plastic and ceramic); access to the school grounds

Speaking scientifically
same, different, materials

Lesson 2: The same but different

Introduction
Show the children each of the floor coverings. Try to have several carpet samples and ask them if they can feel the difference between wool and man-made materials. Ask them if they know where wool comes from. If you have different samples of wooden flooring, ask the children to look at the different patterns of the grain.

Take the children for a short walk through the school and out into the playground. Ask them to look closely at what they are walking on. They might see carpets, plastic tiles, paving stones and tarmac.

Whole-class work
1. Show the children the chairs, plates and chopping boards. They need to be able to touch them.

2. Look at and feel the plates. Make observations about them. Ask: *What is different about them?* The paper plates are flexible and light. The plastic ones will be lighter than the glass, and ceramic ones and may be single, bright colours. The glass ones will usually be clear, but the ceramic plates might be decorated with coloured patterns. Ask: *Which ones do you think will last the longest? Which ones would be easiest to break?*

3. Ask the children what the chopping boards are used for. Some children will recognise them from their kitchen at home. Talk about them needing to be quite strong and heavy. Ask: *Which one do you think will last the longest?*

4. The chairs will have one material that most of it is made of, and then other materials for different parts. For example, a plastic chair might have metal legs.

Individual work
5. Ask the children to draw the following and label all the materials:
● a picture of a chopping board on a table that has been made of at least two different materials and is standing on a floor
● a picture of a chair made of two materials, which is on a floor next to a table made of at least two different materials. On the table is a plate.

6. Ask the children to write down three materials that a table can be made of, three materials that a chair can be made of, three materials that a chopping board can be made of, and three materials that a plate can be made of.

Differentiation
● Support children when they are labelling their drawings and naming the three materials that the four different objects are made of.
● Challenge children to start thinking about why certain materials are used. For example: *Why are most school chairs made of quite hard materials? Why do some parts of the school have hard, plastic flooring, and some soft carpets?*

Science in the wider world
When common objects such as chairs and tables are made, the materials used are usually the most suitable. Children need to begin to understand why certain materials are used and not others.

Review
The children can be assessed on how well they label their drawings and how well they can list the materials that are used for each of the objects.

Objectives
● To understand that spoons made of different materials have different uses.

Resources
A selection of spoons of different sizes (including those made of metal, wood or plastic and those made from a combination of two different materials); a selection of tables and chairs (from the previous lesson)

Speaking scientifically
material, size, usefulness, metal, wood, plastic

Lesson 3: Spoons

Introduction
Remind the children about the different materials that are used to make chairs, chopping boards and plates. Look at a few of the chairs that you used in the previous lesson. Ask the children why they are the shape that they are. Get them to test some of the chairs. Ask: *Which is the most/least comfortable?* Try to find tables that don't match the chairs: they could be too big or too small. Ask: *What problems can you see? Is there an ideal match of chair size to table size?*

Whole-class work
1. Start by asking the children what spoons are used for and make a list on the whiteboard. They should know that they can be used to stir tea, eat cereals, serve meals and mix things together in bowls.

2. Draw a spoon with an extremely long handle next to a tiny bowl. Ask: *Why would it be difficult to use a spoon like this?*

3. Draw a spoon with a tiny handle next to an enormous bowl. Ask: *Why would it be difficult to use a spoon like this?*

4. Ask the children to tell you why a paper spoon wouldn't be very useful. Ask what might happen if a metal spoon were used to stir porridge in a pan (they might not be aware that the spoon will get hot, but they should understand that the spoon might scratch the pan). They should begin to realise that the size and materials of the spoon matter.

5. Show the children the selection of spoons and ask them what they think each one would be used for. Ask for two volunteers to come to the front. Tell one of the children to hold up a spoon that they would eat their cereal with. Tell the other to hold up a spoon that they wouldn't eat their cereal with.

Group work
6. Ask the children to write down the size and the material of each of these spoons:

- a spoon to eat my yoghurt in my lunchbox
- a spoon for a grandfather to stir his tea with
- a spoon to give an elephant its medicine
- a spoon to mix a cake with
- a spoon to serve out spaghetti.

Discuss what they have written: the size of the spoon will be fairly easy to decide but they may have chosen different materials.

> ### Differentiation
> ● Some children will need support when they are trying to write down their choices of spoons, and will need help in deciding the size and certainly the material.
> ● Challenge children to look at spoons using secondary sources. They might be interested in how they are carved by hand.

Science in the wider world
This lesson encourages the children to look at different materials and decide how good they are for making certain objects.

Review
Children can be assessed on whether they identify an appropriate size and material for each of the spoons.

Objectives
● To know that clothes are made from lots of different materials.

Resources
Objects made of plastic, wood and metal; a collection of clothes with labels (including wool, cotton, linen and man-made fibres); a collection of threads (including wool, cotton and nylon – or a similar man-made fibre); pictures of a cotton plant, flax and sheep wool or media resource 'Clothes' on the CD-ROM; contents of the children's PE bags; glue

Speaking scientifically
cotton, wool, linen, polyester, fibres, man-made

Lesson 1: Clothes

Introduction
Show the children the objects made of plastic, wood and metal. Check that they know what each material is called. Ask: *Why haven't you got any metal or wooden clothes?* They should be able to tell you that the materials that clothes are made from are soft and that they bend and are light. They should also know that clothes made of wood or metal would be hard, heavy and stiff.

Whole-class work
1. Show the children the pictures of flax, a cotton plant and some sheep. Ask them what material comes from each of them. They should know that wool comes from sheep but they might not realise that linen comes from flax, or that cotton comes from a plant. Media resource 'Clothes' on the CD-ROM shows images of flax, cotton and sheep wool, and how these materials can be used to make clothes.

2. Show them a piece of clothing that is made of polyester or another man-made fibre. Ask them what they think it is made of. They might think it is wool or cotton, but they need to understand that many of our clothes are made of man-made fibres or are a mix of wool, cotton or linen and a man-made fibre.

3. Show the children some of the clothes and ask them what they think each is made of. Show them where the labels are that say what the material is. Sort the items of clothing into separate piles – one each for linen, wool, cotton, totally man-made, and a man-made/natural fibre mix. At some stage during the lesson ask the children to come and look at each pile and feel the different materials.

Individual work
4. Ask the children to find out what material their T-shirt and PE shorts are made of. Then ask them to look at the T-shirts or tops that they are wearing in the classroom. They should write down and complete a sentence for each item of clothing:

   ● My shorts/T-shirt/shirt is made of _____.

5. Give each child two or three threads of cotton, wool and a man-made fibre. They should be about 10cm long. Tell the children to stick them carefully onto their sheets of paper and to label each thread. Next to each thread they should write down the clothes that they wear that are made of this kind of material. They will need to look at the labels inside their clothes at school and at home. When they have finished find out which is the most common material used.

Differentiation
● Support children who might need help reading the labels in their clothes and completing their sentences.
● Challenge children to find out where angora and cashmere come from and ask them why they think that these materials are expensive.

Science in the wider world
Some materials are cheaper than others to use and to make clothes from. The children should realise that cheaper fabrics are usually those that are man-made in a factory, rather than those collected from plants and animals.

Review
Children can be assessed on how well they complete their sentences and how many clothes they match to the different threads.

Objectives
● To know that toys are made from lots of different materials.

Resources
A collection of toys made from different materials (including wood), each child should bring in a toy from home

Speaking scientifically
manufactured, mould, hard, soft, flexible, moving parts, metal, wood, plastic

Lesson 2: Toys

Introduction
Ask the children: *Why aren't toy cars usually made of cotton, or wool?* They should know that materials like cotton and wool are soft and flexible: the car would flex when they pushed it and the wheels wouldn't roll very well. Ask: *What materials would work better?* They should tell you that metal, wood and plastic are stiff and strong and don't bend or break easily. Explain that glass is also hard and strong. Ask: *Why aren't scooters or skateboards made of glass?*

Whole-class work
1. Show some examples from the collection of toys and ask them to tell you what each is made of. Many will be made of several materials.

2. Discuss why parts that move are often metal. (Metal can be moulded and made to be very smooth, so parts can roll and won't rub.)

3. Why do they think plastic is used so much? (It's cheap, hard-wearing, brightly coloured and easy to mould.)

4. Discuss why toys that are made of wood are more solid and less detailed than ones made of plastic or metal. (Wood can't be melted and poured into a mould.)

5. Discuss rubber. The children should know that most wheels are rubber; look for rubber in the rest of the toys.

Group/individual work
6. Each child should have brought some kind of toy to school. In groups of four, tell them to look carefully at what each toy is made of and to write down all the materials, with the most common at the top of the list and the least common at the bottom.

7. When they have finished ask each group to tell you their most common and least common materials. Produce a whole-class list on the whiteboard and discuss the results: plastic will probably be at the top, for reasons already discussed (price, durability and the fact that it can be moulded).

8. Tell the children that they must choose two of the toys in the classroom. They can be ones they have brought in or ones that you have shown them. They should draw each one on their paper and label each of the different materials.

Differentiation
● Support children who need help labelling their drawings accurately.
● Challenge children to look at small, common objects that aren't toys, such as spectacles, watches, mobile phones and combs. *What materials have been used to make them?*

Science in the wider world
Even small, common objects such as spectacles are made from several different materials, such as glass, plastic and metal. We consume an enormous amount of different materials. How long will the materials last?

Review
Assess the children on how well they complete and label their drawings.

Objectives
● To know that a bicycle is made from a lot of different materials.

Resources
A large adult bicycle; photocopiable page 171 'A bicycle'; rulers

Speaking scientifically
bicycle, metal, plastic, rubber, bicycle parts (saddle, gears, brakes and so on)

Lesson 3: Bicycles

Introduction
Ask the children what bicycles are used for. (Don't show them a bicycle at this stage.) They should know that they are ridden for pleasure and that some people ride them to work, to the shops and so on. Ask them how many bicycles they have seen made of cotton or a mixture of wool and glass. They should realise that bicycles have to be rigid and that, because they have to go over bumps, they can't break easily. Ask the children how a bicycle works. They should know about sitting on the saddle, the pedals turning, the wheels moving and the handlebars helping to steer the bicycle.

Whole-class work
1. Show the children a large adult bicycle. Make sure that they can get close to it and see all the moving parts. Point to some of the parts first without saying anything about the materials that have been used to make them. Show them the saddle, pedals, handlebars, chain, gears and so on and write the names where the children can see them. Ask: *Would you like to ride a bike that is heavy or light? What do you think the gears are for? Where are the gear levers? Why have some of the parts got oil on them.* They need to know that the moving parts have to move easily and that the lighter the bike the better.

2. When they know what all the parts of the bike are called, ask them what they think they are made of. They should see that the frame, pedals, chain and so on are metal and that the mudguards and cables are plastic. Look at the tyres. Ask: *Why aren't they made of wood? Why are they rubber? What is special about rubber?* They should know that it bounces and that balls are often made of rubber.

Group work
3. Give each child photocopiable page 171 'A bicycle'. Ask them to look carefully at the bicycle and identify the material for as many of the parts as possible. For example, a label might read 'mudguard – plastic'. The children should draw a line from each written label to the correct part of the bicycle.

4. When they have finished their labels tell them to colour the bicycle so that the metal parts are red, the plastic parts are blue and the rubber parts are green.

Differentiation
● Support those children who find labelling their bicycle difficult. They will have to be reminded of what the parts are called as well as the materials that the parts are made of.
● Challenge children to look at very early bicycles such as boneshakers and penny farthings. They were made from different materials. *Why weren't some of the parts made of plastic, like modern bicycles?*

Science in the wider world
This is another example of our need for a wide range of materials. If we didn't have such a range of materials, bicycles would look very different.

Review
Children could be assessed on how well and how accurately they complete their photocopiable sheets.

Objectives
● To know that some materials are used to help us to keep warm.

Resources
A large picture of people in polar or mountaineering clothing; a large picture of sunbathers and people in shorts and T-shirts; examples of clothes that we use to keep us warm (hats, coats, gloves, boots, scarves); coloured pencils

Speaking scientifically
warm, cold, temperature

Lesson 1: Keeping warm

Introduction

Show the children a picture of people dressed in polar or mountaineering clothes. Ask: *Are the people in the picture going to explore the desert?* They should realise that they are wearing clothes that keep them warm. Ask: *How do you know that the clothes the explorers are wearing will keep them warm?* They will probably have hoods, gloves and thick boots. Perhaps they are wearing animal skins with the fur showing.

Show the children the picture of the people who are sunbathing and wearing shorts. Ask: *Do the people in the picture live at the North Pole? How do you know?* The children should be able to tell you that in certain weather conditions we have to wear warm clothes, but when it is warm and dry such warm clothes aren't necessary.

Talk to the children about low temperatures and freezing winds and the dangers of not being able to stay dry. We need to wear clothes that will help us to stay warm and dry in very cold and wet weather.

Whole-class work

1. Show the children each of the warm weather clothes in turn – the scarf, coat, boots, hat and thick trousers. Ask them to tell you what part of the body each item helps to keep warm. Ask all the children to write down and complete these sentences:

- I wear gloves to keep my _____ warm.
- I wear waterproof _____ to keep my feet warm and dry.
- My thick _____ keeps my body warm.
- My scarf keeps my _____ warm.
- If I want to keep my legs warm I wear thick _____.

Individual work

2. Ask the children to use their paper to draw themselves dressed to go out in really cold weather. Discuss what they think they should be wearing: their drawing must include a woolly hat, thick gloves, a scarf and boots.

3. When they have finished their drawings tell them to label the clothes they have drawn.

4. Tell the children to make a list of the clothes they are wearing today. Ask them to look at the labels and see what their clothes are made of. Are they clothes to keep them warm or clothes to keep them cool? What is the weather like? Are they all wearing appropriate clothes?

> **Differentiation**
> ● Support children who find completing the sentences and labelling their drawings difficult.
> ● Challenge children to find out what kind of clothing and protection climbers on Mount Everest need to stay warm.

Science in the wider world

We are not equipped to live in very cold conditions and we have to use different materials to help us to stay warm – and alive. Some natural materials, like wool, and some man-made materials, such as Gore-Tex®, help to keep out the wind and the cold.

Review

The children can be assessed on how well they complete their sentences and how accurate their labels are on their drawings.

Objectives
● To know that metals are used for many things.

Resources
A few metal objects (food cans, other small tins, bracelets, watches, knives, forks, garden tools); photocopiable page 172 'Marvellous metal'; a selection of coins from different countries; clipboards; black wax crayons; access to the school grounds

Speaking scientifically
metal, silver, iron, steel, gold, brass, copper, tin, lead

Lesson 2: Metals

Introduction
Take the children for a walk around the school and the school grounds and ask them to write down everything they observe that is made of metal. During the walk encourage the children to look at both large and small things: staples and drawing pins as well as window frames and car bodies. When they return to the classroom talk about what they have found and write the names of the objects where all the children can see them. Take some of the examples and ask them whether they could be made of a different material. For example, ask: *Could a staple be made of woollen thread? Could a window frame be made of paper? Could a window frame be made of wood? Could a hammer be made of glass? Why? Why not?*

Whole-class work
1. Metal as a material is not always the same and includes lead, steel, bronze, brass, copper, gold and so on. Show the children the assortment of metal objects – but don't show the coins at this stage.

2. Talk to the children about metal being able to be shaped and pressed into all kinds of different shapes.

3. Ask the children to describe the metal in each of the objects and ask the same question for each of them: *Could this object be made of any other material?*

Individual work
4. Ask the children to draw a metal object that they think should only be made of metal. Tell them to write why they think it is best made of metal.

5. Show the children lots of different coins and tell them that metal can be pressed into round shapes and then the pattern of each coin can be pressed into the surface of the metal.

6. Give them paper and black wax crayons and show them how to 'rub' the coins so that the pattern appears on the paper. These rubbings can be mounted as a display.

7. Try to borrow brass rubbings or take the children to a local church where they will be allowed to rub the brasses there.

8. Give the children photocopiable page 172 'Marvellous metal' and ask them to complete it.

Differentiation
● Brass rubbing or rubbing coins can be difficult and some children may need help with this. Support children when they are completing their photocopiable sheets.
● Challenge children to find out about the Bronze Age or the Iron Age and to find metal objects that are made of iron and bronze.

Science in the wider world
Metal is a natural object. It has to be dug out of the ground and made into the objects we use. If it starts to run out, we will need to recycle metal more and use scrap to make the things we need.

Review
The children can be assessed on how well they complete their photocopiable sheets.

Objectives
● To know that wood has many uses.
● To know that wood comes from trees and that woods from different types of tree are not the same.

Resources
Some wooden objects, including some that are partly made of wood (a pencil, garden fork, trowel, chair, wooden spoon, toys, a wooden box); some pieces of bark; cross sections of wooden branches; large black wax crayons; magnifying lenses; coloured pencils; clipboards; photocopiable page 173 'Wonderful wood'; access to the school grounds

Speaking scientifically
wood, bark, grain, texture

Lesson 3: Wood

Introduction
The children need to know that wood is a living thing and that all the objects they have that are made of wood have been made from something that was once alive. Take the children for a walk around the school grounds to look for objects that are made of wood. Don't forget to look at small objects, such as pencils, and large pieces of wood, such as telegraph poles. Explain that buildings need huge beams made of wood to hold up the roof.

Whole-class work
1. You will need to find different trees close to the school. Show the children how to take bark rubbings using paper and black wax crayons. Use the rubbings to mount a display with the names of the different trees alongside the rubbings. You might be able to find oaks, beeches and sycamores.

2. In the classroom show the children some of the objects that are made of wood. Ask: *Could a wooden spoon be made of paper instead? Could it be made of plastic or metal? Could a wooden chair be made of cotton or wool? If not why not?*

3. The children should understand that wooden objects are hard and rigid. Things like boxes and spoons could easily be made from metal or plastic instead and some solid objects can be made from two materials, such as wood and metal.

Individual work
4. Ask the children to use the magnifying lenses and to look at the pieces of bark, cross sections of branches, or the boxes and spoons. Tell them about the grain of the wood and ask them to draw what they see through the magnifying lens. These drawings can be part of a class display on materials.

5. Ask each child to complete photocopiable page 173 'Wonderful wood'. When they have finished make sure that you discuss the children's answers with the whole class. They will have tried to suggest where wood is used and why it is used. But wood is used less and less; the children need to be asked whether wood really needs to be used or whether another material could be used instead.

Differentiation
● Some children will need support when completing the photocopiable sheet.
● Challenge children to find out which wood is used to make telegraph poles and why that kind of wood is used. Ask them to find out what the hulls of sailing ships were made from and why. They could also research paper – what it is and how it is made.

Science in the wider world
Making objects from wood means either chopping down trees or recycling old wood. In order to preserve forests, recycling should become more and more important. Paper is made from wood and this needs to be made from as much recycled material as possible.

Review
The children can be assessed on how well they complete the photocopiable sheet.

Lesson 1: Soil

Introduction
Take the children into the school grounds to collect two different samples of dry soil. Back in the classroom look at one of the samples and ask: *What do you think this is made from?* Record their answers on the whiteboard. They should understand that soil started off as rock that has been eroded and broken up into smaller pieces over a long, long time. Ask: *Why is soil important?* Remind the children that plants need soil to grow.

Whole-class work
1. Ensure that each group of four has two different samples of dry soil. They must be kept apart. Ask the children to separate each of the samples into different parts. They should find large and small pieces of grit and pebbles, bits of vegetation and even the odd insect.

2. Ask them to suggest ways of recording their observations and how they might display the results of their investigation.

3. Ask them whether they think their soil samples are different. If they are different, what exactly are the differences? Explain that there are different types of soil and that these are suited to different types of plant.

Group work
4. Give each group of four two plastic containers and check that they still have two separate samples of soil, together with something to stir their soil and water mixes. Put about 10cm of each soil mix into separate containers and cover each one with plenty of water so that the soil samples are completely submerged. Each sample needs to be stirred well and then stirred again a few hours later and then again the next morning. Leave them undisturbed for at least two days.

5. After the soil and water mix has been left undisturbed for two days, each child can complete photocopiable page 174 'Soil investigation'. Ask the children to look carefully at the layers of sediment and to talk again about what they think soil is made from. They should be able to see the grit and pebbles at the bottom and the different layers of fine sand-like material suspended in the water.

Differentiation
● Some children will need help with the vocabulary. They may also need help to express their ideas when they are describing their soil.
● Challenge children to use microscopes to look at some of the soil particles. It will open up a new world of sand grains and even minute insects. Drawing some of these will produce a brilliant display.

Science in the wider world
We all need plants like wheat and rice, and animals that we eat need grass. These plants grow in soil so it is important that we know what soil is and how to keep it healthy so that more plants can grow.

Review
Children can be assessed on how well they complete the photocopiable sheet.

Objectives
● To know that mammals, birds and insects use materials.
● To find out which materials are good insulators.

Resources
Pictures and books showing wasp, bumble bee, hamster, mouse and birds' nests; if possible, find an abandoned birds' nests and a wasps' nest; small glass jars with lids; materials to use for insulation (cotton wool, straw, polystyrene, an old jumper); warm water; thermometers; photocopiable page 'The life cycle of a bird' on the CD-ROM

Speaking scientifically
insulate, natural materials

Lesson 2: Nests

Introduction
Show the children the pictures, or real examples, of nests. Don't show birds' nests at this stage. For each example ask: *What kind of animal do you think made this nest? What is it made of?*

Ask: *Why do some animals build nests?* Show a birds' nest. Discuss how the nest helps to keep the eggs warm and protects the eggs and the young birds: use photocopiable page 'The life cycle of a bird' from the CD-ROM to revise this.

Whole-class work
1. Look closely at different birds' nests. Talk to the children about the kinds of materials the birds have used to make them. Some nests are carefully made with the material woven together and lined with dried mud. Others are untidy platforms of twigs; but they all serve the same purpose.

Group work
2. Organise the children into groups of four or five and give each group a different type of insulating material. Ask them to think of a simple test they could carry out to find out which material keeps the nest warmest.

3. Explain that they will be using small jars of warm water to represent the eggs. Try to ensure that each group's water starts off at the same temperature. Each group needs to wrap their jar of warm water in their insulating material and then measure the temperature of the water every two minutes and write it down. This needs to happen about five times.

4. While the children are waiting to take the temperature, ask them to draw a birds' nest with eggs in it. They should label the materials the nest is made from and describe what the nest is used for.

5. When the temperature has been measured several times, look at the results and work out which nest has stayed warm for the longest – or which one has cooled down the slowest. Ask: *Which material was the best insulator?* Explain to the children that although birds use different materials in their nests to help their eggs stay warm, they still have to spend a lot of time sitting on their eggs.

Differentiation
● Some children will need support to structure the test and measure the temperature. They might need to be told what to expect so that they understand the idea that their jar of warm water will start to get colder despite the insulation.
● Challenge children to look at insect nests. A wasps' nest is made out of chewed leaves and wood and is a perfect structure of hexagonal cells. If you can get hold of an abandoned one, the children could draw it and find out more about how it is made.

Science in the wider world
It is not just humans that use materials to keep them warm and protected. Birds and insects make nests out of all kinds of natural materials that are available.

Review
Children could be assessed on how well they draw their birds' nest and how accurately they explain what it is for. They could also be assessed on how well they carry out their test and how accurately they record data.

Objectives
● To understand why different materials are used for different things.

Resources
A selection of different objects (a table knife, jumper or shirt, mug, bicycle, hosepipe, hammer, light bulb, fishing float, nail, sheet of paper); large sheets of art paper; small sheets of paper; pencils; coloured pencils; scissors; glue

Speaking scientifically
appropriate material, iron ore, coal

Lesson 3: Using materials

Introduction
At the top of the whiteboard write: tree, corn, iron ore, coal.

At the bottom of the whiteboard write: electricity, newspaper, cooking oil, paper clip. Read out the words and ask the children to match the words at the bottom to the material they have been made from at the top. Ask some children to explain their answers to the rest of the class.

Whole-class work
1. Hold up some of the objects that you have collected and ask the children what each one has been made from. They should be able to do this easily as they have seen many of the objects before.

2. Explain that you have made some of the objects from different materials and you are not sure that they will work as well. They should tell you why the following objects made from the new material won't work as well as the originals: Plasticine® knife, steel jumper, cardboard mug, rubber bicycle, glass hosepipe, polystyrene hammer, iron light bulb, concrete fishing float.

Group work
3. Divide the children into groups of four or five and give each group a large piece of paper, several smaller pieces of paper, scissors, glue and pencils. Tell them that they have to invent a house in a new world called Strange Land, where everything is made out of the wrong material. Explain that, as well as all the furniture and equipment, they have to put an adult in their room who will be wearing clothes made from inappropriate materials. On the smaller pieces of paper they should draw the person, the furniture and anything else that they think they will need – but everything has to be made out of an inappropriate material.

4. Each individual drawing should be stuck onto the group's large piece of paper and labelled. Labels might include: a paper table, a grass door, a rubber kitchen knife, a glass bed with metal duvets.

5. When each group has finished ask them to swap their sheets with other groups to look at and discuss. They could be used for a large classroom display.

Differentiation
● Support children who might have difficulty in recognising the 'wrong' materials and how to spell them.
● Challenge children to look at how some materials are used. Paper and cardboard, for example, can be used for all kinds of things – including furniture; metal can be made into huge ships and tiny pieces of jewellery.

Science in the wider world
This lesson builds on previous lessons and once again encourages the children to consider properties of different materials. Some uses of materials are obvious, but some materials can be surprisingly versatile: heavy metals can be used to make delicate objects; straw can, in fact, be used to make strong and durable houses.

Review
The children can be assessed on how inappropriate the materials in their imaginary room are.

Objectives
● To understand that some materials are natural and that others have to be manufactured.

Resources
A range of materials (wood, stone, wool, cotton, silk, sand, coal, natural sponge); coloured pencils

Speaking scientifically
natural, manufactured, material

Lesson 1: Natural or manufactured?

Introduction
Talk about wood. Make sure that the children know that it comes from trees but can be shaped, sawn and stuck together to make doors, tables and so on.

Talk about stone and explain that it is dug from the ground in quarries. It can be shaped into blocks for building or thinner sheets for paving. It can also be shaped into sculptures.

Whole-class work
1. Help the children to understand the differences between raw materials and manufactured (man-made) materials and objects. Start by explaining that iron ore is dug from the ground and heated to high temperatures until the iron melts. It can be mixed with other metals to form (manufacture into) bronze, tin and so on. Ask the children to look quickly round the room and remind themselves of a few of the metal objects that they use all the time. They should realise that these range from large table legs to small pieces of metal such as door hinges, staples and paper clips.

2. Show them the wool and make sure they know it comes from sheep and has to be spun (manufactured) into jumpers. Ask: *Do you know where cotton and silk come from? Why do you think silk is so expensive?* If possible show them caterpillars that make silk.

3. Look at the sand, which is a natural material. Ask: *Do you know what sand turns into when it is melted?* Make a list of things that are made from glass.

4. Look at the coal. Ask: *Do you know where this comes from? What is it used for?*

5. Look at the sponge. Ask: *Do you think this is alive, has never been alive or is no longer alive?* Most children will not realise that sponges are living creatures from the sea.

6. Many things that the children use are made from plastic because it can be moulded into many different shapes. Explain that plastic is made from oil, which is also used to make petrol.

Individual work
7. Write a list of raw materials and manufactured objects on the board: glass bottle; diamonds in a diamond ring; oil; steel; iron ore; gold ring; plastic duck; woollen jumper; bag of flour; aluminium can; coal; salt; milk; petrol; silk scarf.

8. Give each child some paper, pencils and coloured pencils. Ask them to draw three natural materials under the heading 'Natural materials' and three manufactured materials, or objects, under the heading 'Manufactured materials'.

Differentiation
● Support children who might have difficulty choosing those materials that are natural and those that are manufactured. They may also find reading some of the names of the materials difficult.
● Challenge children to find out about manufacturing processes. For example: how paper is made; how oil is drilled and turned into petrol; how teaspoons are made.

Science in the wider world
Some of the resources that we use could become scarce. Oil will not last for ever and yet it is used to make petrol and plastics. Perhaps we shouldn't take them both for granted.

Review
Children can be assessed on how well they choose the natural and manufactured materials.

Objectives
● To know the different materials needed to make a cake.
● To know that the materials need to be mixed and heated and placed in a container to make a cake.

Resources
Enough muffin cases and tins to cook one cake per child with a few spare cakes (at least one for each table); a large mixing bowl; wooden spoons; ingredients to make the cake (currants, sultanas, raisins, mixed peel, glacé cherries, zest of half a lemon, plain flour, cinnamon, butter, soft brown sugar, eggs); photocopiable page 'Cake recipe' from the CD-ROM; adult volunteers; an oven

Speaking scientifically
ingredients, heat, heated, cool, change, hygiene

Lesson 2: Making a cake

Introduction
Tell the children that they are going to help bake a cake. All the ingredients should be on a table where the children can see them. Show them all the different ingredients and ask them what each material is. They should realise that the currants, raisins, sultanas and cherries are fruits that have been dried, and that lemons come from plants. Where do they think the flour and sugar have come from? They should realise that they have both come from plants too.

Ask: *What do you think will happen to all the different materials? Once the cake is cooked will it be possible to get any of the ingredients back again? Will the flour still be the same? Will we be able to get the eggs back?*

Whole-class work
1. Provide each table with a copy of the cake recipe, or display it on the whiteboard. Make sure the children have washed their hands and be aware of any allergies. If any of the children are allergic to any of the ingredients find an alternative recipe.

2. Make enough of the cake mix for one cake for every child, with a one spare one for each table. Let as many children as possible help with the weighing and mixing. Allow them to look carefully at the fruit and other ingredients and let them feel the flour and sugar.

Group/individual work
3. When the cakes have been cooked and are cool make sure that every child has one of the cakes to take home and that each table has one spare cake.

4. Ask the children what they think happened to the materials in the oven and whether they think the flour and sugar, for example, could now be taken out of the cake.

5. Let the children take their spare cake to pieces and look at what has happened during cooking.

6. Ask them to write down three sentences explaining what they did and what happened. Tell them to drawn the original ingredients and the finished cakes.

Differentiation
● Some children will need support when they are trying to describe what happened during cooking – especially when they are writing their sentences.
● Challenge children to find out how bread is made and how the process is different from making a cake. Try making bread in the classroom.

Science in the wider world
It is important that children learn to cook. If they realise that cooking and science are closely linked it might make them more enthusiastic.

Review
The children can be assessed on how well they describe the process of mixing and cooking the cakes.

Objectives
● To understand that if we freeze some materials they change into something else.

Resources
Ice-cube trays with prepared ice cubes (enough for each child); small containers for their ice cubes; ice-lolly moulds (two for each child); different prepared fruit juices in jugs that pour well (blackcurrant, orange, ruby grapefruit)

Speaking scientifically
water, ice, change, freezing, frozen

Lesson 3: Ice lollies

Introduction
Talk to the children about what happens to water when it gets really cold. They should know that it freezes because they will have seen ice in winter. But, they should also know that ice can be useful. Ask them how ice is used. They should be able to tell you about freezers being used to keep food cold. In other words, it is a way of keeping food fresh for a long time.

Ask the children to describe water – show them some by filling a jug from the tap and pouring it into glasses for some volunteers to drink. They should realise that it is fluid and that it moves as it is poured. Ask them to describe ice. They should tell you that it is hard and slippery and so solid it doesn't move. Remind them that when they made their cakes, the flour and butter and eggs changed when the mixture was heated and it was impossible to get them back again. Talk about how water changes to ice when it freezes but then turns back to water as it warms up. The act of freezing water is not irreversible.

Whole-class work
1. Give each child a couple of ice cubes in small containers. Tell them to leave them in the containers during the lesson to watch what happens.

2. Give each child an ice-lolly mould and a couple of spare moulds for each table. Show the children how to pour the flavoured water into their moulds and then place them in a freezer.

3. Ask them how they might make a striped ice-lolly. They will have to pour a small amount of flavoured water into the mould then freeze it, then pour a different colour in and freeze that until they have the number of stripes they need. This takes a long time, but is worth the wait.

Individual work
4. Ask the children to use some paper to describe what they did. Tell them to try to use at least three sentences and labelled drawings that show how water can be flavoured and then frozen. They could draw their finished ice-lollies – or, better still, they could draw themselves enjoying their ice-lollies.

5. They should have also watched their ice cubes melt back into original water again and could explain this on paper too.

> ### Differentiation
> ● Some children will need support in drawing and labelling diagrams that show the process of flavoured water freezing into an ice-lolly.
> ● Challenge children to make ice-lollies with vertical stripes. Challenge them to find out about glaciers and icebergs.

Science in the wider world
Ice is essential as a food preserver if we want such a wide range of things to eat. Ice as glaciers and icebergs is melting faster than it was in the past. The children will eventually need to start understanding some of the issues related to global warming.

Review
The children can be assessed on the accuracy of their drawings and writing about their ice-lollies.

SUMMER I

Objectives
● To assess whether the children know that there are many different materials that we see every day.

Resources
Photocopiable page 175 'Materials all around'; access to the school grounds

Speaking scientifically
● To use their observations to suggest answers to questions.

Materials all around us

Revise
● Tell the children that you are going to ask them really quick questions and that you want really quick answers. Each time you ask a question you will ask five children for one answer each.
● All the questions will be about materials. Ask the children how many materials they can think of. They should be able to list all of the ones that you will be asking questions about: plastic, rock, metal, wood, fabric, paper, rubber and glass.
● Tell them to stay in their seats and ask five children this question about each of the materials: *What can you touch without leaving your seat that is made of _____?*
● Ask the children to move out of their seats and stand in the classroom. This time ask five children this question about each of the materials: *What can you see around the classroom that is made of _____?*
● Take them into the playground or some other part of the school and ask five different children this question about each of the materials: *What can you see in the playground that is made of _____?*

Assess
● The children should have been able to give you some of the answers but there might be gaps in the kinds of materials that they can see and touch, or there might not be many plastic materials in the playground. Similarly, there might not be many objects made from rock in the classroom. Rubber might be the least common material in both the classroom and out in the school grounds.
● Give each child the photocopiable page 175 'Materials all around' and explain to them how to do each of the three surveys.
● The objects that they find that are made from different materials might be slightly different, but the material that is the most common and the one that is the least common should be the same.

Further practice
● The next logical step and one that has been covered in previous lessons is to make sure that the children know that many different objects are made from more than one material. For example, bicycles and toys are a mixture of plastic, metal and rubber, and even simple objects such as knives and forks often have plastic handles and metal tines and blades.

Objectives
● To assess whether the children know that some everyday objects are made from lots of different materials.

Resources
Pictures of, or real, complex but common objects (such as cars, buses, a vacuum cleaner, the inside of an old radio); interactive activity 'What is it made from?' on the CD-ROM

Speaking scientifically
● To use their observations to suggest answers to questions.

Using different materials

Revise

● Looking at the pictures and asking questions about the different materials that have been used to make each object will be effective, but showing the children the actual object so that they can touch it and look closely at what it is made from is even better.

● If possible, take the children into the school car park to look at cars. They should know that the body is metal, but go further than in previous lessons and ask them what the inside of the doors is made from. If they look closely at them they should see metal handles as well as plastic. Ask: *What about the windows? Have you noticed the rubber seals? Where else is there rubber? Where is fabric used?* (They should notice the carpets and the roof lining.) They won't be able to see the petrol, but remind them what makes the car go and that petrol comes from oil.

● Vacuum cleaners can look like Space Age machines. Try to show the children one of the multi-coloured, complex ones. Show them how it works and then let them look at it for a few minutes. Ask them to list all the materials they think the vacuum cleaner is made from – starting from the plug and electrical flex. You could also remind them that the electricity that powers the vacuum cleaner is often created by coal. Ask them what coal and oil have in common. They should know that they are both found in the ground.

● If you can get hold of a few old electrical goods – toasters, radios, hairdryers and so on – the children will be fascinated if they are allowed to take them apart. With supervision and a few different sized screwdrivers they should be able to look inside and see the range of materials that are needed to make something that they take for granted. Sort the materials into piles – one for plastic, one for metals, one for rubber and so on.

Assess

● During the revision part of this lesson the children should have looked in much more detail at the materials that some common objects are made from. When they complete this assessment, expect some interesting choices of object. In fact, look for different choices rather than the more common ones.

● Give each child a piece of paper and ask them to write down these materials on the left-hand side: wood, glass, plastic, metal, paper, rock. Make sure that they leave space alongside each of the materials.

● Tell them to write three things that are made from each of the materials and to underline the object or part of an object that they think is the most unusual.

● The children could also complete interactive 'What is it made from?' on the CD-ROM.

Further practice

● Children like taking things apart and some common objects are really interesting to look at. For example, some of the parts in hairdryers and toasters have been moulded into interesting shapes. They can be looked at closely and drawn. If you have strong glue and lots of adult help it is possible to make unusual sculptures that will make an innovative classroom display.

Comparing the uses of materials

Objectives
● To assess whether the children know that materials have different uses and that some materials change because of heat and cold.

Resources
Some common objects (such as a spoon, gloves, mug, cake, pair of scissors); photocopiable page 'Comparing materials' from the CD-ROM

Speaking scientifically
● To use their observations to answer questions.

Revise

● Try to get the children to realise that they need lots of different materials every day and that they use many different materials from the moment they get out of bed in the morning.

● Ask them to think about the materials that they have used since they got up this morning. Allow them about five minutes to talk about this with the person sitting next to them and with the other children on their table.

● Share some of the materials with the whole class. For example, the clothes they put on, water used for washing, plastic toothbrushes, ceramic dishes and mugs, metal in the car or all the different materials on their bikes when they travelled to school, the materials used for the roads and the pavements. Remind them that they use all these materials all the time, every day.

● What if these materials that they have described aren't used properly? Show them a spoon and say that from now on spoons will only be made from paper. Ask them to describe the problems if this happened. Repeat this for jumpers and gloves made of tin, mugs made of Plasticine®, scissors made of milk, and cakes made with sand instead of flour.

Assess

● The children should know that the reason we use certain materials – like all the different materials that can be used for spoons – is because they work. Wooden, metal or plastic spoons work, but a paper one wouldn't; ceramic mugs work but a Plasticine® one wouldn't.

● Give each child paper and pencils and ask them to complete the photocopiable sheet 'Comparing materials' from the CD-ROM.

Further practice

● The idea that materials change can be explored further. For example, water to ice and then to water again can be seen to happen in winter and is easily done in the classroom. But there are other changes that are important but that we can't see because they happen in factories, for example: sand to glass; oil to petrol; iron ore to steel; oil to plastic; wood to paper and so on.

Name: _____   Date: _____

Describing materials

■ Draw pictures of each material in the correct sorting rings.

(wood)   (cotton)   (paper towel)   (rubber)

(polythene)   (plastic)   (bottle)   (rock)

Hard

Soft

Waterproof

Absorbs water

Bendy

Stiff

Dull

Shiny

I can describe the properties of materials.

How did you do?

In the classroom

- How many different materials can you see in this picture?
- Add as many labels are you can.
- Colour in the picture.

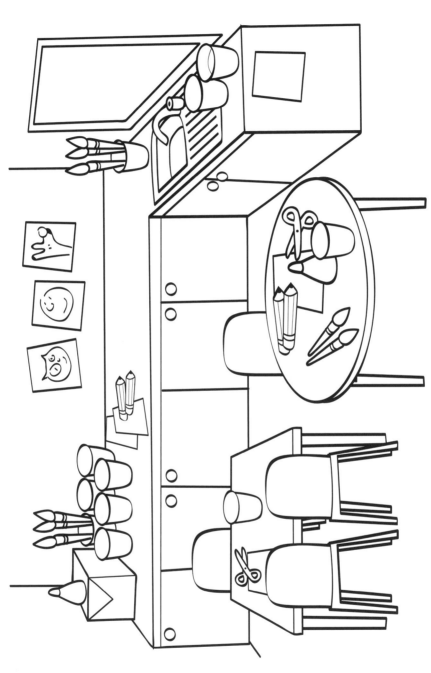

I can identify the materials objects are made from.

How did you do?

Name: _____

In the kitchen

- How many different materials can you see in this picture?
- Add as many labels are you can.
- Colour in the picture.

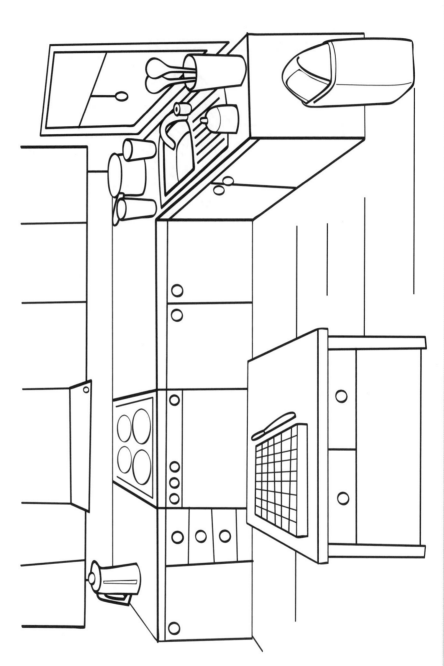

I can identify the materials objects are made from.

PHOTOCOPIABLE

■SCHOLASTIC
www.scholastic.co.uk

A bicycle

- What is a bicycle made from?
- Label all the different materials.

I can identify the materials used to make a bicycle.

How did you do?

PHOTOCOPIABLE

Marvellous metal

■ Collect as many of the following metal objects as possible, and then complete the table.

nail	paper clip	drinks can	coin	key	dish
necklace	piece of wire	I kg weight	scissors	spoon	

Metal object	Why is it made of metal?	What other material could be used?
paper clip	It's strong. It's flexible, so can be bent.	plastic

I can say why objects are made from metal.

How did you do?

Wonderful wood

- Collect some pieces of wood, and objects made of wood.
- Complete the activities below.

I. Examine each piece of wood with a lens and write down everything you notice about the appearance, pattern and texture of wood.

_____

_____

_____

2. Think of situations where wood is important, and complete the table below:

Situation	Where wood is used	Why wood is used
building houses		
kitchen equipment		
in the classroom		
toys		
in the garden		
in the bedroom		

I can ...

How did you do?

Soil investigation

- Leave your soil for two days.
- Then draw what you see and add labels.

Soil sample 1   Soil sample 2

Describe what is the same and what is different about the two soil samples.

Both soil samples: _____

_____

_____

The differences are: _____

_____

_____

I can record my observations.

How did you do?

PHOTOCOPIABLE

■ SCHOLASTIC
www.scholastic.co.uk

Name: _____   Date: _____

Materials all around

- Look for things made of different materials around the school.
- Complete the table below.

Material	Things I can touch without leaving my seat	Things I can find around the classroom	Things I can see from the playground
plastic			
rock			
metal			
wood			
fabric			
paper			
rubber			
glass			

I can identify the materials objects are made from.

How did you do?

Uses of everyday materials and their properties

Expected prior learning

- Know the names of some common materials.
- Know some of the uses of materials (for example, wood for chairs, plastic for bottles, metal for window frames).
- Understand that materials can occur naturally and also be man-made.
- Understand that different materials have different properties.
- Understand that the shape of some materials can be changed using different forces, such as pulling and pushing.
- Understand that certain materials are better for some objects than others.

Overview of progression

After completing this chapter the children should know about:

- sorting materials by their properties
- changing materials by using forces such as twisting, bending, stretching and squashing
- the work of three famous inventors (Dunlop, Macintosh and McAdam) who changed materials so that they could be used in different ways.

Creative context

- This topic provides opportunities for children to make observational drawings and models. They will also begin to learn some basic cooking skills.

Background knowledge

Different materials have a range of different properties. The nature of these properties will determine what forces can be applied to the materials. These forces include bending, stretching, twisting and squashing. Using these forces will change the shape of the materials. In some cases these changes will be permanent, while in other cases the material will revert to its original shape once the force has been removed.

Several famous inventors used these changes to produce different materials, or used common materials in different ways to make products that are used in everyday life today.

Speaking scientifically

- The children should know the names of a range of different materials (cotton, wire, dough, paper) and the forces that will be applied to them (pulling, twisting, kneading, squashing).

Preparation

You will need to provide: a wide range of materials that can be stretched, pulled, bent, twisted or squashed, such as elastic bands, pipe-cleaners, wool, string, cotton, ribbon, shoelaces, garden wire; shoes with lace holes; a broom handle; play dough or modelling clay, rolling pins, cutters, safe knives and lolly sticks; large toy car; knitted jumper; kitchen foil; tights; drinking straws; balloons; safety goggles or glasses; ingredients and equipment to make bread including, plain bread flour, salt, dried yeast and sugar, access to an oven and adult helpers; twist-wrapped sweet, spiral pasta, spiral-bound book; photos of early and modern bicycles, tricycles and ride-ons; bicycle inner tubes; bicycle pump; air mattress and foot pump; balloon pump; waterproof coat; squares of cotton and polythene; kitchen towel; water sprays; trays; pea gravel, larger stone chippings, flat pieces of wood, garden rake and a muddy outdoor area.

On the CD-ROM you will find: interactive activity 'Three discoveries'

■SCHOLASTIC

Chapter at a glance

Week	Lesson	Curriculum objectives	Objectives	Main activity	Working scientifically
1	1	• To identify and compare the suitability of a variety of everyday materials for particular uses.	• To investigate the properties of different materials.	Using a range of materials to test their suitability as a lace for a shoe.	• Identifying and classifying. • Performing simple tests.
	2	• To find out how the shapes of solid objects made from some materials can be changed by squashing, bending, twisting and stretching.	• To investigate how the shape of a material can be changed by stretching it.	Testing how far elastic bands will stretch and measuring the results.	• Performing simple tests. • Gathering and recording data to help in answering questions.
	3	• To find out how the shapes of solid objects made from some materials can be changed by squashing, bending, twisting and stretching.	• To investigate how the shape of some materials can be changed by twisting, bending, stretching and squashing them.	Using different forces on pliable materials such as play dough or modelling clay. Creating a range of different shapes and constructing a model.	• Using observations to suggest answers to questions.
2	1	• To find out how the shapes of solid objects made from some materials can be changed by squashing, bending, twisting and stretching.	• To investigate how the shape of some materials can be changed by twisting or stretching them.	Using forces on different materials to find out which force changes the shape of the material.	• Performing simple tests.
	2	• To find out how the shapes of solid objects made from some materials can be changed by squashing, bending, twisting and stretching.	• To investigate how forces such as pulling, stretching, squashing and kneading can permanently change the shape of some materials.	Making dough and cooking bread rolls.	• Observing closely, using simple equipment.
	3	• To find out how the shapes of solid objects made from some materials can be changed by squashing, bending, twisting and stretching.	• To investigate twisting as a force to change the shape of some materials.	Investigating materials to see whether change is permanent or not after a force has been applied. Making a model using twisting as the main force.	• Observing closely.
3	1	• To find out about people who have developed useful new materials.	• To explore how Dunlop invented inflatable tyres. • To be able to explain how the pneumatic tyre/air cushioning aids comfort.	Listening to the story of how Dunlop invented pneumatic tyres. Investigating ways to inflate an inner tube, air mattress and balloon.	• Observing closely, using simple equipment.
	2	• To find out about people who have developed useful new materials.	• To explore how Macintosh used rubber and cloth to create waterproof clothing.	Listening to the story of how Macintosh invented waterproof clothing. Undertaking a simple experiment to test the effectiveness of a waterproof membrane.	• Observing closely, using simple equipment. • Using observations and ideas to suggest answers to questions.
	3	• To find out about people who have developed useful new materials.	• To explore how McAdam used a mixture of natural materials to change how roads were made.	Listening to the story of how McAdam invented a new way of building roads. Using similar methods and materials to make a simple 'road' in the playground.	• Observing closely, using simple equipment.

Objectives
● To investigate the properties of different materials.

Resources
Photocopiable page 190 'Shoelaces'; materials for making laces (string, garden wire, ribbon, wool, cotton thread, elastic; shoes with lace holes

Speaking scientifically
material, flexible, properties, guess

Lesson 1: Everyday materials

Previous knowledge
This chapter builds on the previous chapter's investigations into the properties of materials and why items are made from particular materials.

Introduction
All the threads, ribbons and garden wire should be cut into suitable lengths ready for testing and threading through the lace holes. Tie and untie the original laces in the shoe a few times so that the children can see what you are doing. Ask them to describe the shoelace and what you need to be able to do with it. It needs to be long enough to thread through the holes and thin enough as well as being flexible enough to bend and stretch. Ask the children to tell you what 'flexible' means: it needs to be able to bend round corners, twist into bows and knots, and be strong enough not to snap.

Whole-class work
1. Show the children the different materials you have gathered (string, garden wire, cotton thread, wool, ribbon, elastic) and ask them which ones they think could be used for shoelaces.

2. They should realise that some materials are more flexible than others and can be easily tied into bows.

3. Similarly they should realise that even though some might bend (such as cotton and garden wire), they might not bend enough or they might be too thin.

Group work
4. Provide each group of three or four with samples of each of the materials and a shoe (with the laces removed) to practise with.

5. Provide each child with photocopiable page 190 'Shoelaces'.

6. Ask them to try each of the materials on the shoes and then complete the photocopiable sheet. They need to decide whether each of the materials will actually work.

7. Before they give each material a score out of 10 they will need to discuss with their group whether or not the material will make a good shoelace.

8. Compare each group's results and decide which material makes the best shoelace.

Introducing the new area of study
As you begin to investigate the areas of squashing, bending, twisting and stretching through the next few lessons, you should begin to introduce the idea of forces and how they relate to the materials you are investigating and their particular properties. Identify what is happening to the materials you are working with in simple terms such as pushes and pulls. Have the children been pushing or pulling the shoelace materials in this exercise? What properties did the materials demonstrate? Repeat this pattern of questioning throughout the next five sessions to get the children used to the idea of thinking about how forces act on materials. You can also introduce the idea of reversible and irreversible changes. Is the change that the children have made to the materials they are investigating permanent, or could the materials go back to their original state?

Differentiation
● Support any children who might find threading and tying cotton difficult.
● Challenge children to use more strands of cotton and wool. Ask: *What happens if several strands of cotton or wool are twisted together? Does it make it stronger? Is it still flexible enough to use? Can it still be bent and tied? Are three or four strands twisted together better for shoelaces?*

Science in the wider world

Materials have to be fit for purpose and shoelaces have to work – and to
continue to work day after day. Children will be familiar with the idea of
twisting, bending and tying and should recognise many of the properties that
shoelaces must have. It is also important that they understand some of the
properties that are *not* needed. For example, shoelaces don't need to be able
to be stretched or squashed and if they were hard and solid they wouldn't
work.

Review

Children could be assessed on their knowledge of the properties of shoelaces:
what shoelaces need to be able to do, and what properties are not needed.

Objectives
● To investigate how the shape of a material can be changed by stretching it.

Resources
Photocopiable page 191 'Fair test'; piece of strong wire; broom handle; shoe and elastic band that fits the lace holes; elastic bands of various widths; rulers; paper; weights; safety glasses

Speaking scientifically
stretch, stretching, pull, force, altered/changed, elastic

Lesson 2: Stretching shapes

Introduction
Show the children the wire and broom handle and ask them whether they could stretch each one by pulling it. Now show them the elastic band that was tried out as a shoelace in the previous lesson. Ask them why it didn't work properly even though it fitted the holes in the shoe and was the right length. They should remember that, although elastic can be pulled, twisted and bent, it stretches too easily and is difficult to tie accurately.

Whole-class work
1. Show the children the selection of different elastic bands of various widths (they must all be complete loops) and ask them which one they think will stretch the longest. They should know that this will be the thinnest one.

2. Ask them how they can prove this and talk about pulling the elastic band in some way.

Group work
3. Organise the class into groups of three or four children. Ensure the children know to keep their faces away from the elastic bands and wear safety glasses when testing them. Provide each group with a selection of elastic bands, a weight that can be hung from them, a ruler and some safety glasses. Ask them to talk about how they can show which elastic band will stretch the furthest.

4. Once they have finished their discussion, talk about what the groups have decided. Make sure that all the groups are using the same method to test the elastic bands.

5. The best way to test how far the elastic bands will stretch is, wearing the safety glasses, to hold each elastic band over the edge of a table, hang the weight on it, and then use the ruler to measure from the edge of the table to the bottom of the stretched elastic band.

6. Each group should complete the tests and write down their measurements on a sheet of paper.

Individual work
7. Give each child photocopiable page 191 'Fair test'. Tell them that they must complete the sheet on their own, but that they can discuss with the rest of their group what they will write in each section before filling it in.

> ### Differentiation
> ● Support any children who may experience difficulty in completing the photocopiable sheet.
> ● Challenge more confident learners to test the elastic bands by using a force meter.

Science in the wider world
When materials are pulled, bent, twisted or squashed they often change shape permanently but elastic bands go back to their original shape when the force is removed. This happens to some extent to other materials such as sponges (squashed and then released) and paper which, when twisted and bent, can be flattened back to its original shape.

Review
Children could be assessed on how well they understand what a fair test is and their understanding of elasticity – that some materials possess elasticity while others don't.

Objectives
● To investigate how the shape of some materials can be changed by twisting, bending, stretching and squashing them.

Resources
Photocopiable page 192 'Models'; elastic bands; garden wire; paper; woollen thread (or an old woollen jumper); play dough/modelling clay; rolling pins; cutters; safe knives; lollipop sticks

Speaking scientifically
shape, model, squeeze, squash, twist, stretch, pull, push, roll, press, tear

Lesson 3: Making models

Introduction
Show the children the elastic band, garden wire, paper and woollen thread (or old jumper). Ask them what they can do to each of them to make them change shape.

For example, stretching and twisting the elastic band will change its shape; the garden wire can be bent and twisted; the paper can be squashed and the wool/jumper can be stretched, bent and twisted.

Whole-class work
1. Show the class the play dough or modelling clay. (Good quality pliable clay that is not wet or sticky is more easily shaped and can be kept and displayed.)

2. Ask the children for suggestions as to how they could alter the shape of the material. Encourage them to use the correct vocabulary, such as roll, push, press, squash, pinch, pull, stretch and cut.

3. Demonstrate some of the forces they suggest and show how each one can alter the shape of the material.

Individual work
4. Give each child a piece of play dough/modelling clay about the size of a tennis ball and all the tools they will need, such as rolling pins, cutters and so on.

5. Ask them to reshape the material in as many ways as they can. They can cut it into cubes, roll it into balls or sausages, flatten it into discs, cut small pieces and twist them into spirals.

6. After five to ten minutes ask the children to use whatever forces they need to push, squash or press the pieces into the shape they started with.

7. Next, give each child photocopiable page 192 'Models'. Tell them that you want them to use the play dough/modelling clay to make a model. It can be a figure (such as a person), an animal or a fantasy monster. Ask them to think about the forces they will use to make their model.

8. After they have finished making their model, tell them to draw their model and to label the different parts saying what they did to make each part. For example, a head has to be squashed and rolled, arms will have been rolled and stretched and so on.

> ### Differentiation
> ● Support children who need help in making their model. They might also need help in labelling their drawings accurately.
> ● Challenge children to use a wide range of forces to make their models. For example, you could ask them to include a shape that has been twisted, squashed or pulled.

Science in the wider world
All the forces the children will have used are also used to manufacture various objects. It will be useful to talk about wood being turned on a lathe to shape chair legs, and iron and steel being pulled and stretched to make wire, or squashed and moulded to make flat sheets or panels for car doors. Children need to be aware that all these forces change the shape of materials into objects that we need.

Review
Assess the children on their understanding of the actual forces that they have used. For example, do they know how to effectively roll, twist and squash the material they are using?

Objectives
• To investigate how the shape of some materials can be changed by twisting or stretching them.

Resources
Photocopiable page 193 'Stretch and twist'; large toy car; wool or acrylic jumper; a collection of objects and materials that can be stretched, squashed, squeezed and twisted (elastic bands, kitchen foil, tights, pipe-cleaners, drinking straws, wire, wool, paper, balloons, sticky tape); safety glasses

Speaking scientifically
push, pull, twist, stretch, flexible

Lesson 1: Twisting and stretching

Introduction

Remind the children that forces make things move, slow down, speed up and stop. Ask for volunteers to use a force to make the large toy car move (they should push it). Ask them how they can use a force to make it go faster and stop. Remind them how they used forces of pulling, twisting and stretching when they tied the shoelaces (lesson 1, week 1), when they found out which elastic band stretched the furthest (lesson 2, week 1) and when they made their model in lesson 3, week 1.

Whole-class work

1. Show the children the collection of objects and ask them to predict whether they will be able to twist or stretch each of the materials without breaking it.

2. Some materials such as the tights and the elastic band can be twisted and stretched but the woollen thread will only stretch very slightly.

3. Discuss why materials that the children wear (such as wool for jumpers, and nylon for tights and shirts) have to be able to stretch and move. They should understand that if the materials that clothes were made from didn't stretch they would be very difficult to wear.

4. Show them the acrylic or wool jumper and ask for volunteers to pull it, bend it and stretch it. Talk about why jumpers aren't made from wood or glass or tin foil.

Group work

5. Give each group of three or four children a set of these items: elastic band, kitchen foil, tights, pipe-cleaner, drinking straw, wire, wool, paper, balloon, sticky tape and safety glasses to wear when conducting their tests.

6. Provide each child with photocopiable page 193 'Stretch and twist'. Tell them that they can talk within their group about each of the objects as they try to stretch and twist them, but they should complete the photocopiable sheet on their own.

7. When they have finished, ask them to check that they have all written similar answers.

> **Differentiation**
> • Support children who find writing down their answers difficult. They could draw the objects in the appropriate places on the photocopiable sheet instead of writing their names.
> • Challenge children to look more closely at what they wear. Some materials, such as for heavy winter coats, will be less flexible than others. Ask them to find out where the clothes they wear have to be able to move, bend or stretch. (The clothes will have to move where their bodies move and bend: for example, knees, elbows and shoulders.)

Science in the wider world

Children will be aware of how to twist and bend, squash and tie, but need to know that these are all forces that, when applied to materials, change their shape – sometimes permanently and sometimes not. For example, it would be extremely difficult if we buckled a belt in the morning and then found that it stayed fixed like that and couldn't be unfastened.

Review

Assess the children on how good they are at predicting how different objects and materials can be made to change by twisting, bending or stretching them.

Objectives
• To investigate how forces such as pulling, stretching, squashing and kneading can permanently change the shape of some materials.

Resources
Photocopiable page 194 'Making bread'; one piece of play dough/modelling clay; all the ingredients to make enough dough for the whole class (for enough dough for four to five children to make a small bread roll each provide: 700g plain bread flour, 2 teaspoons salt, 2 teaspoons dried yeast, 2 teaspoons sugar, approx 425ml warm water); access to an oven, baking trays, baking parchment, mixing bowls, floured surfaces; adult helpers

Speaking scientifically
ingredients, dough, squash, press, pull, twist, crush, knead

Lesson 2: Squashing and kneading

Introduction
Show the children a piece of play dough/modelling clay and ask them what they could do to make it change its shape. Remind them that when they made their models in week 1, lesson 3, they twisted, squashed, pulled, rolled and cut the material.

Whole-class work
1. Show the children the separate ingredients to make bread rolls. Explain what each ingredient is. Tell them that by mixing all the ingredients together they will make dough. Then, by squashing and kneading the dough they will make it into the shape of bread rolls.

2. Remind the children of food hygiene and how they must wash their hands before handling the ingredients and use clean utensils.

Group work
3. Assign an adult helper to each group. The helper should show the group how to make the dough by mixing all the dry ingredients in a bowl and then adding warm water. This needs mixing together with a wooden spoon and then by hands.

4. The adult helpers should then show the children how to knead the dough on a floured surface. When the dough is reasonably pliable, give each child a small piece to make one bread roll. Ask them to knead the dough.

5. Ask them what they are doing. They should be squashing, kneading, pulling and twisting the dough for about three minutes until it is elastic and can be pulled and stretched easily without breaking.

6. Tell each child to squeeze and shape the dough into a ball shape. Label the balls in some way and leave them to rise in a warm place for about 90 minutes.

7. Provide each child with photocopiable page 194 'Making bread'. They should use diagrams and labels to write how they made the bread.

8. When the dough has risen, it has to be squashed and kneaded again for about two minutes, then shaped back into balls and placed on a baking tray lined with baking parchment. Use a soft pencil to write each child's name on the baking paper next to their ball of dough.

9. Bake the bread for approximately 20 minutes at 200°C (Gas Mark 6), watching it carefully so that it doesn't overcook.

10. As the children eat their rolls, discuss how they have changed the shape of the dough to make their finished bread.

Differentiation
• Support children who need help writing their instructions on how to make the bread, using the appropriate scientific vocabulary.
• Challenge children by discussing non-reversible change. The shaped dough can be taken back to its original shape quite easily but once the ingredients are mixed together and cooked there is no way that any of the dry ingredients can be changed back into their original forms.

Science in the wider world
Cooking and baking usually involve irreversible change, and means mixing ingredients together by stirring and squashing and kneading. Children should know that these forces will alter the shape of the material that they are using.

Review
Assess the children on how well they understood how they made the bread and the kinds of forces that they used when they were mixing the dough.

Objectives
● To investigate twisting as a force to change the shape of some materials.

Resources
Pencil and pencil sharpener; twist-wrapped sweet; spiral pasta; spiral-bound book; pipe-cleaners; scrap materials; coloured paper; threads; scissors; glue

Speaking scientifically
twist, spiral, spin, material, force, knot

Lesson 3: Shapes with a twist

Introduction
Remind the children that in a previous lesson (week 1, lesson 1) they had tested materials to find out which made the best shoelace. They should remember that it was string/wool or similar that worked best. Point to a shoelace on a child's shoe and ask them what you have to do to it, so that it fastens the shoe. They should use vocabulary such as threading, pushing, pulling and so on. When they tell you that it is tied in a bow, make sure that they realise that you are twisting and knotting the lace.

Whole-class work
1. Remind the children that when you untie a shoelace it returns to its original shape. Show them a sweet wrapped in paper. Point out that the paper has been twisted at each end. Ask: *Do you think the twist is permanent?* Show that it is not by untwisting the paper and carefully flattening it. Then ask: *What about spiral pasta – can that be returned to an original shape? What do you think will happen when it is cooked?*

2. Sharpen a pencil and show the children the twist of pencil shaving. Also show them the way metal wire has been twisted into shape to hold a spiral-bound book together.

3. Next, show the children some pipe-cleaners. Hold several in your closed hand with the ends sticking out. Ask volunteers to pull an individual pipe-cleaner out of your hand. They should find this easy to do.

4. Tell the class that twisting the pipe-cleaners makes them stronger. Invite volunteers to change the shape of some of the pipe-cleaners by bending and twisting them. Finally, twist several pipe-cleaners tightly like a rope and hold them in your closed fist. Invite volunteers to try to pull one out of your hand, as they did before. They will find it is impossible to separate one pipe-cleaner and pull it out from the twisted group.

Individual work
5. Make sure that each table has pipe-cleaners, a selection of scrap materials, threads, coloured paper, glue and scissors. Tell the children that they are going to make and dress a pipe-cleaner person such as a doll, a footballer, dancer or soldier.

6. Remind them that they will need to twist the pipe-cleaners to join them together and that the twists should make them stronger and hold together better.

7. Use the completed models as part of a classroom display.

Differentiation
● Support children who might find twisting and shaping their models difficult.
● Challenge children to look at different kinds of knots, and to tie them. Show them how to plait three strands of wool.

Science in the wider world
Some materials such as ships' hawsers are made of twisted metal wire that becomes stronger as it is twisted. Some materials are manufactured into spirals such as pasta shapes and springs.

Review
Assess the children on how well they understand that some materials can be twisted and made stronger, but that other materials are able to revert back into their original shapes.

■SCHOLASTIC

Lesson 1: Dunlop and his tyres

Objectives
● To explore how Dunlop invented inflatable tyres.
● To be able to explain how the pneumatic tyre/air cushioning aids comfort.

Resources
Images of early and modern tricycles/ride-on vehicles; bicycle inner tubes and bicycle pump; air mattress and foot-pump; balloons and balloon pump; drawing materials; pictures of cyclists and bicycles

Speaking scientifically
rubber, glue, pneumatic, inner tube, air pressure, pump, inflate, valve, rough, smooth

Introduction
Check whether any children have rubber or latex allergies before introducing these materials to your classroom. Show the class some images or real examples of children's ride-on vehicles and ask them to describe what it feels like to move along on one. Display images of early tricycles/bicycles and invite the children to comment on similarities and differences between these. Ask how it would feel to ride on one of the older versions and encourage them to consider the difference that modern wheels would make to the comfort and smoothness.

Whole-class work
1. Tell the class the story of John Boyd Dunlop and the invention of the inflatable tyre. The idea of inflating tyres with air came to him while watching his young son ride on his tricycle. Dunlop realised that his son was feeling every bump in the road because the solid rubber tyres on the tricycle did not provide any cushioning. He came up with the idea of gluing thin rubber sheets around the wheels and inflating these with air. The world's first successful pneumatic tyre had been invented! He patented his invention and a local firm agreed to build bicycle frames which would fit the new tyres.

2. Show the children some bicycle inner tubes. Explain that they are usually hidden inside the tyre to make a cushion between it and the metal rim of the wheel. Point out the valve and demonstrate how to attach the pump and begin to inflate the tube. Invite children to take turns working the pump and feeling how the inner tube changes as the air inflates it.

3. Talk about experiences of camping holidays or sleepovers where children have slept on an air mattress. Talk about the difference a well-inflated mattress can make.

Group work
4. Explain the group activities around which the children are going to rotate. Show a flattened camping air mattress attached to a foot pump and tell them to take it in turns to try to inflate it.

5. Set up one or two bicycle inner tubes with pumps attached to the valves and challenge the children to inflate these. Fix balloons over balloon-pump nozzles and tell the children to see how much they can inflate these.

Independent work
6. Display images of mountain-bike riders cycling over rough terrain. Talk about how the wide tyres help them ride over stones and ruts and ask the children to make drawings of these bicycles. Encourage them to think in particular about what the tyres will look like and what sort of ground they are riding over.

> **Differentiation**
> ● Support children by providing them with pictures of bicycles to cut out and glue onto a sheet of paper to make a composition of riding cyclists.
> ● Challenge children to write about Dunlop and the invention of pneumatic tyres.

Science in the wider world
Air pressure is measured in psi (pounds per square inch). Wide, knobbly mountain bike tyres require inflation to around 30 psi – depending on conditions, while race bike tyres are often inflated to around 120 psi to reduce rolling resistance.

Review
Children could be assessed on their observations about the difference air cushioning can make to objects and whether they can give an oral or written account of Dunlop's invention.

Objectives
● To explore how Macintosh used rubber and cloth to create waterproof clothing.

Resources
Waterproof coat; school jumper; small cotton squares; polythene; kitchen towel; water in small containers with spray tops; trays

Speaking scientifically
materials, cloth, waterproof, plastic, rubber, elastic, brittle, vulcanisation

Lesson 2: Macintosh and waterproof clothes

Introduction
Show the children an obviously waterproof coat and a school jumper. Ask them which one they would wear if it was raining. They should be able to tell you that they would wear the waterproof one. Ask: *What do you think 'waterproof' means?* Talk about some of the names of waterproof coats, such as parkas, cagoules, raincoats and so on. Tell the children that lots of waterproof coats or raincoats used to be called macs or mackintoshes, named after the man who invented them – Charles Macintosh.

Whole-class work
1. Tell the children that Charles Macintosh was born in Glasgow in 1766. In 1823 he patented a way of making cloth waterproof. He found that if rubber was sandwiched between pieces of cloth it could be used to make coats that were waterproof. Macintosh used natural rubber from trees. However, it was sticky, became brittle when it was cold and was not very elastic, so it didn't stretch and move very easily. In fact, his early waterproof clothes were a bit smelly, very stiff and tended to melt in hot weather. Nearly 20 years later a new method was developed where the rubber was mixed with other materials and went through a chemical process known as 'vulcanisation', which made the rubber more durable and easier to use.

2. Nowadays we use all kinds of materials that are waterproof and rubber has been replaced by different materials including plastic.

3. Tell the children that it in the following group activity they are going to show how Macintosh's method of making cloth waterproof actually works.

Group work
4. Make sure that each small group has two squares of kitchen paper, two small squares of cloth (preferably cotton), a small square of polythene slightly larger than the cotton square, a container of water with a spray top, and a tray to prevent the water from spreading.

5. Tell the children to place a square of kitchen paper on the tray and a piece of cloth on top. Ask them what will happen when the cloth is carefully sprayed with water. They should be able to tell you that the water will go through the cloth and wet the paper towel. Let them try this and see what happens.

6. Now dry the tray and this time place a sheet of paper towel on it, then the cloth with the square of polythene on top. Ask: *What do you think will happen this time when water is sprayed onto the materials?* The children should realise that the water won't get through the polythene and this means that the cloth is waterproof.

Differentiation
● Challenge children to find out more about Macintosh and vulcanisation. They might also be able to find out more about modern waterproof materials such as Gore-Tex® and how they work.

Science in the wider world
Macintosh put two materials together and changed them into something different. Modern waterproofing uses all kinds of different materials but plastics and rubber are still used for such things as pond linings and damp-proof courses on buildings because water can't get through them.

Review
The children could be assessed on their understanding of how Macintosh made the first waterproof coat.

Objectives
● To explore how McAdam used a mixture of natural materials to change how roads were made.

Resources
Pea gravel and larger stone chippings; flat pieces of wood slightly less that 1m long; garden rake; access to the school grounds

Speaking scientifically
roads, gravel, stones, tar, tarmac, smooth, hard, surface, camber

Lesson 3: McAdam's roads

Introduction
Talk to the children about how they came to school that morning. Ask them whether they drove, cycled or walked over mud and potholes and got their shoes filthy or their cars splattered with mud. Ask: *Why not?* They should be able to tell you that the surfaces of the roads and paths were smooth and hard. Tell them that this surface is made from a hard substance called 'tarmac' that is named after its inventor, a man called John McAdam.

Whole-class work
1. Tell the children that John McAdam was born in 1756 in Ayr, Scotland. He was the youngest of ten children. When he grew up he became an engineer and road builder. McAdam noticed that the stagecoaches (which were the usual way of travelling over long distances at that time) used roads that were often just potholed, rutted tracks that became muddy and sometimes impassable during bad weather. He realised that to get round this problem, roads needed to be slightly raised above the surrounding ground and made from a more durable material.

2. McAdam took two different materials – small pieces of chipped rocks and then smaller gravel-sized pieces. The chipped rocks were placed on the road surface and the smaller gravel-sized pieces were placed on top and pressed down to make a harder surface. He decided that this surface should be slightly curved (known as the 'camber' of the road) to allow the water to drain off instead of making puddles on the top.

3. All our modern-day roads have a camber so that rainwater drains into the gutters at the sides of the roads. They are also made in a similar way to McAdam's roads, except that we use tar on the top to bind the stones together (tarmac – shortened from tarmacadam) and make a hard surface.

4. Take the children outside to a small area of the playground that is not covered by tarmac and is muddy with ruts and holes. It should not be smooth or flat. Ask them to imagine what it would be like if the whole of the playground was like that or all the roads were as muddy and full of ruts and holes.

5. Show the children how McAdam's roads were made. Start by inviting some volunteers to put down a layer of stone chippings. When there are enough, rake it as smooth as possible and place some planks of wood on top of the chippings. Ask a group of children to stand on the wood to flatten the layer underneath.

6. The final step is to remove the wood and add a layer of pea gravel, pressing it down firmly. Try to show the children what the camber of the road means.

Differentiation
● Challenge children to find out more about modern road construction – what materials are used, how the roads are laid down and how are they similar to and different from McAdam's original idea.

Science in the wider world
Roads are good examples of how we use a range of different materials to create something that is vital in the modern world. Now our roads are smooth and easy to use, but it is still the case that simple materials like stones, sand and concrete are made into something that is smooth and hard-wearing.

Review
Children could be assessed on how well they understand how McAdam made his roads and how his idea was developed to create a harder-wearing surface.

● To remember the properties of materials they have investigated.
● To match materials to their properties.
● To suggest why objects are made from certain materials.

Resources
Photocopiable pages 195 and 196 'Changing shapes' (1) and (2); flat piece of wood; piece of cloth; pipe-cleaner; sheet of paper; elastic band; ball of modelling clay; cotton or woollen fabric; coat or jumper; metal wire; shoelace

Speaking scientifically
bend, twist, squash, stretch, flexible, elastic, rigid, forces pulling, pushing, turning

Changing shapes

Revise

● Show the children a flat piece of wood (such as a piece of plywood or a bookshelf) and a piece of cloth. Ask: *Which of these materials would make the best clothes?* They should be able to tell you it is the cloth and tell you why by using vocabulary such as flexible, soft, stretchy and so on. They should also know that cloth will fit the way that our bodies bend and stretch and will return back to its original shape.

● Talk to the children about the inflexible wood. Ask them why it is better for such things as bookshelves. They should be able to tell you that it is rigid and won't bend or stretch. Ask questions such as: *What would happen if you made a shelf out of wool? What would happen if you made a school sweatshirt out of a sheet of metal or a piece of hard plastic?*

● Show the children each of the following materials in turn and talk about how their shapes can be changed: pipe-cleaner, sheet of paper, elastic band, ball of modelling clay, piece of cotton or woollen fabric, coat or jumper, metal wire, shoelace.

● Ask the children how they can change the pipe-cleaner's shape. They should remember (or know) that it can be twisted and bent but not stretched or squashed. It is possible to return it to its original shape.

● The sheet of paper can be squashed and twisted and, with some creasing, can be made flat again. The elastic band can be stretched, squashed, twisted and bent but will quickly return to its original shape. The ball of modelling clay can be squashed, bent, stretched and twisted, but will have to be pulled, pushed and squashed back into its original shape. The fabric will be slightly stretchy and will bend and twist, returning back to its original shape (as will the coat or jumper). The metal wire can be bent and twisted, as can the shoelace. However, the wire is more difficult to bend and twist into shapes such as knots.

Assess

● Provide each child with photocopiable pages 195 and 196 'Changing shapes (1)' and 'Changing shapes (2)'. Before asking them to complete the activity, show them an example of each of the materials/objects displayed on the sheet and make sure that they can recognise them.

● Remind the children that the shape of most of the objects can be changed by several different forces. For example, a piece of cotton could be bent, twisted and squashed.

Further practice

● Many objects that are used by the children involve the shape of materials being changed using machines. There may be DVDs and online examples of how some objects are made. Examples of this include: turned wooden chair legs, wire stretched from hot metal, spiral book binding, fabrics being spun and woven, pizza dough being kneaded and so on.

● Challenge the children to look around the classroom, at home and at their cars and bicycles. Can they identify objects where the materials have been changed by being squashed, stretched, twisted and bent?

Objectives
● To recall how materials have been changed or used together in different ways.
● To recall how pneumatic tyres, waterproof clothing and modern road surfaces were invented.

Resources
Photocopiable page 197 'Three discoveries'; interactive activity 'Three discoveries'; pictures of an early bicycle and a modern bicycle; bicycle tyre and pump; waterproof coat; small pieces of stone and pea gravel

Speaking scientifically
pneumatic, tyres, inflate, waterproof, rubber, vulcanise, road surface, camber, Dunlop, Macintosh, McAdam

Three discoveries

Revise
● Remind the children of what Dunlop, Macintosh and McAdam made by recapping the stories and asking them questions. Each of the three inventors took materials and changed how they were used to make something new.
● Dunlop noticed that riding a bicycle was difficult and uncomfortable. Show the children pictures of early bicycles/tricycles. Ask: *Why would it have been uncomfortable to ride a bicycle like this?* Point out that the tyres were hard and solid – they were made from either wood or solid rubber.
● Dunlop used rubber sheets and glued them on to the wheel and then pumped them full of air. Ask: *Why would these pneumatic tyres be better for the rider?* Show the children how to inflate a bicycle tyre. Remind them that although the tyre is still made of rubber, the layer of air has a cushioning effect which makes the bicycle more comfortable to ride.
● Next, show the children a waterproof coat. Talk about how coats like this protect us from rain and keep us dry. Remind the children that they are made from all kinds of materials that are specially designed to keep out water.
● Charles Macintosh found that if he put a layer of rubber between pieces of material in a kind of sandwich he made the material waterproof. Eventually, a new process was developed (vulcanisation), which made the rubber better to use to make waterproof clothes that were flexible and easy to wear. These raincoats were often called macs after Macintosh.
● John McAdam changed how roads were built. Ask the children what roads were like before he started changing how they were made. They should remember that they were rough, muddy and full of holes.
● McAdam used a layer of larger stones followed by a layer of smaller gravel to construct his roads. Remind the children what the layers of stone and gravel looked like when they constructed their mini-road in a previous lesson.
● McAdam also made the roads higher in the middle and sloping down at each side. This was the camber and allowed water to run off the roads and into the gutter.
● Ask the children: *What are roads and school playgrounds like now?* They should remember that we still use McAdam's method of using gravel and stones but nowadays there is an additional layer of tar on top. This is often called 'tarmacadam' (or just tarmac).

Assess
● The children can work their way through their interactive activity, 'Three discoveries' on the CD-ROM to check their understanding. Alternatively, provide each child with photocopiable page 197 'Three discoveries'. They need to write down what they know about the three inventions and draw and label simple diagrams to show how they were made.

Further practice
● A display of different types of bicycle tyres (mountain bikes, racing bikes) and pictures of different car tyres will show children how far the design of tyres has changed since when they were first used.
● There are all kinds of modern waterproof materials. Gore-Tex® is a good example, but many people wear coats made from material that has been waterproofed by coating it with wax. This is very similar to Macintosh's original invention.
● If there are roadworks near the school and a hole in the ground, it may be possible to take the children to see the different layers that make up the foundation of a modern road.

Name: _____   Date: _____

Shoelaces

■ Try to use each of the materials you have been given as a shoelace.

■ Then tick the boxes below and give marks out of ten to show the results of your findings.

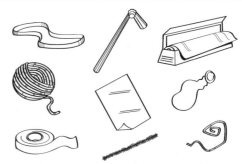

Object	Thin	Bendy	Strong	Marks out of ten
Wool				
String				
Wire				
Elastic				
Ribbon				
Cotton thread				

I can test materials and record my answers.

How did you do?

PHOTOCOPIABLE

■SCHOLASTIC
www.scholastic.co.uk

Fair test

■ Answer questions 1 to 4 below before you start testing your elastic bands.

■ Answer question 5 after you have finished testing the elastic bands.

1. What are you trying to find out? _____

_____

_____

2. What do you think will happen? _____

_____

_____

3. What equipment will you use? _____

_____

_____

4. What do you need to keep the same to make the test fair?

_____

_____

_____

5. What did you find out? _____

_____

_____

_____

I can carry out a fair test.

How did you do?

Models

■ When you have finished making your model, draw it in the space below.

■ Label the different parts and write what you did to make each part.

I can identify forces.

How did you do?

SCHOLASTIC
www.scholastic.co.uk

Stretch and twist

■ Which of these items can be stretched and which can be twisted? Indicate your answer by writing an 'S' or 'T' beside each item.

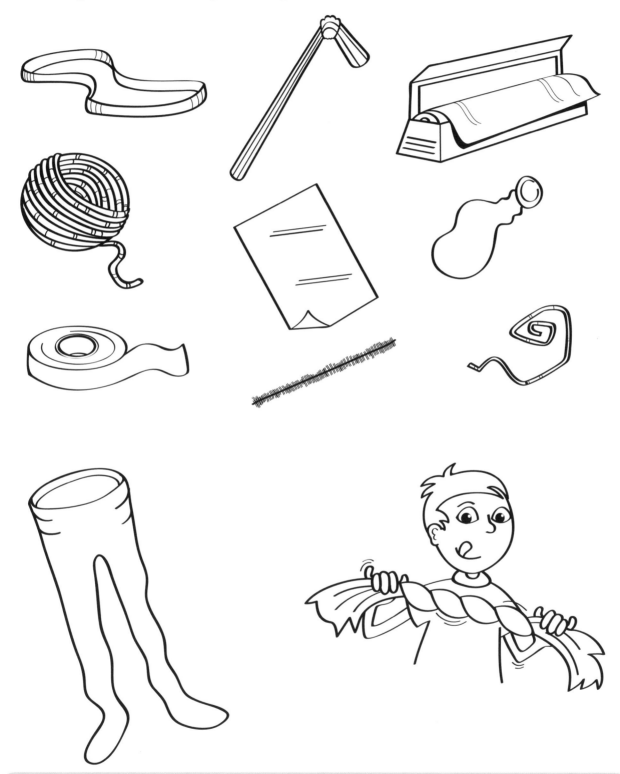

I can investigate whether objects can be stretched or twisted.

How did you do?

Making bread

- Write instructions about how you made the bread rolls.
- Use diagrams and labels to show what you did.

First I...

Then I...

After that I...

I can record what I did.

How did you do?

PHOTOCOPIABLE

SCHOLASTIC
www.scholastic.co.uk

Changing shapes (1)

■ Look at each of these materials and write in the boxes how each of them could be changed by choosing to twist, bend, stretch or squash it.

■ Draw what the object/material would look like after you have changed its shape.

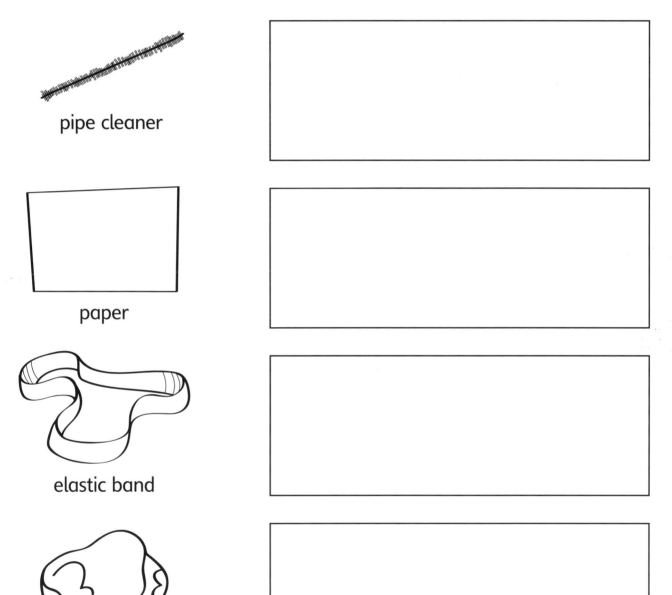

pipe cleaner

paper

elastic band

modelling clay

I can identify forces.

How did you do?

Changing shapes (2)

■ Look at each of these materials and write in the boxes how each of them could be changed by choosing to twist, bend, stretch or squash it.

■ Draw what the object/material would look like after you have changed its shape.

cotton fabric

woolen jumper

metal wire

shoelace

I can identify forces.

How did you do?

Three discoveries

■ Write and draw the discoveries that each of these three people made.

■ Explain what they did and how they did it.

Dunlop

Macintosh

McAdam

I can describe how three new discoveries were made.

How did you do?

PHOTOCOPIABLE

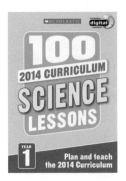
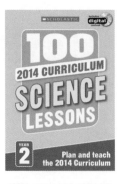
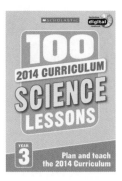
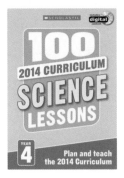
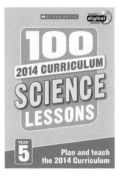
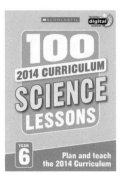
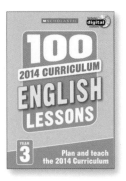
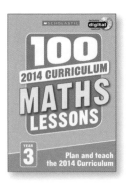
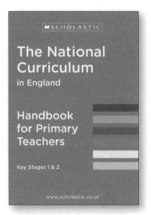